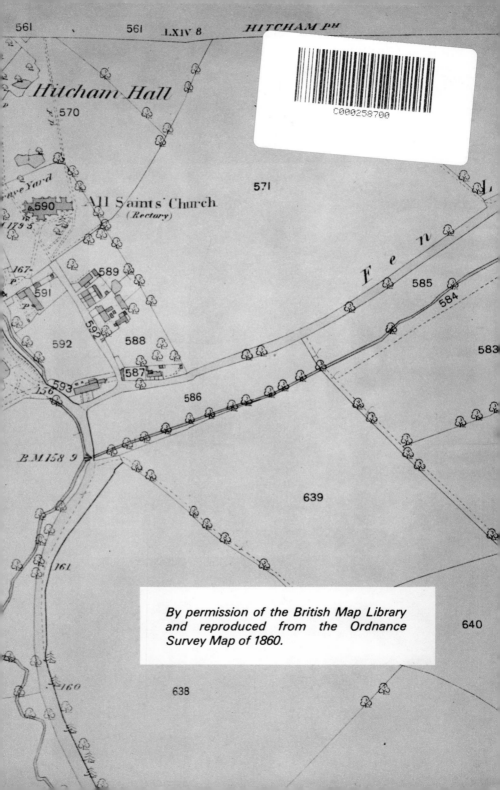

561   561   LXIV 8   HITCHAM PH

Hitcham Hall

570

Grave Yard

△590

179·5

·167·

All Saints' Church
(Rectory)

571

591

589

592

592

588

587

592

156

593

586

BM 158·9

161

F e n

585

584

583

639

640

·160

638

Ex Libris

Bramble & Comma butterfly

A. D. MARSHALL
HATFIELD.

HENSLOW OF HITCHAM

HENSLOW OF HITCHAM

Botanist, Educationalist and Clergyman

by

JEAN RUSSELL-GEBBETT

TERENCE DALTON LIMITED
LAVENHAM . SUFFOLK
1977

Published by
TERENCE DALTON LIMITED
LAVENHAM . SUFFOLK
ISBN 0 900963 76 X

Drawings on pages 28, 73, 118 by Caron Robinson.

Text photoset in 10/11pt English

Printed in Great Britain at
THE LAVENHAM PRESS LIMITED
LAVENHAM . SUFFOLK

Contents

Index of Illustrations...   7

Chapter One   The Man, His Times and His Task   9

Chapter Two   A Cambridge Apprenticeship   15

Chapter Three   The Parish School and Other Charities...   ...   29

Chapter Four   Botany Teaching in a Village School   42

Chapter Five   Botany Teaching and the Nation   60

Chapter Six   Adult Education in the Village—Exhibitions and
Expeditions   74

Chapter Seven   Science and the Farmers   91

Chapter Eight   Museums for the People   97

Chapter Nine   A Reflection   119

Appendix I   121

Appendix II   122

References   124

Index   135

Index of Illustrations

Section I

(i)   John Stevens Henslow
(ii)   Frances Harriet Hooker
(iii)   Joseph Dalton Hooker
(iv)   Charles Darwin
(v)   Charles Cardale Babington
(vi)   Marble bust of John Stevens Henslow
(vii)   Bottisham Hall
(viii)   St John's College, Cambridge
(xix)   "Henslow Common Informer"

Section II

(x)   Hitcham House
(xi)   Hitcham Church
(xii)   Hitcham charities
(xiii)   School nomination ticket
(xiv)   School botany pamphlet
(xv)   Daffodil Narcissus
(xvi)   Common mallow
(xvii)   Common ash
(xviii) Oat
(xix)   Wheat rust and mildew
(xx)   Ploughing certificate
(xxi)   Handbill for Hitcham show

Section III

(xxii)   Henslow's Walk
(xxiii) Rules for Visitors to the Botanical Gardens, Cambridge
(xxiv)   Coprolites
(xxv)   The educational collections in the South Kensington Museum
(xxvi)   Ipswich Museum
(xxvii) Membership ticket for Ipswich Museum
(xxviii) List of subscribers to Ipswich Museum
(xxix)   Museum, Kew
(xxx)   Recompense for work for Paris Exhibition
(xxxi)   The Royal Children
(xxxii) Botany lessons for the Royal Children

To my mother

CHAPTER ONE

The Man, His Times and His Task

He [Professor Henslow] was a first rate man of science, an indefatiguable parish priest, an amiable, large-hearted, generous and genial man . . . and a thorough, earnest and practical Christian.
Illustrated London News (Supplement), 22.6.1861.

During the years I associated so much with Professor Henslow, I never saw his temper even ruffled. He never took an ill-natured view of anyone's character, though very far from blind to the foibles of others. It always struck me that his mind could not be ever touched by any paltry feeling of vanity, envy or jealousy. With all this equability of temper and remarkable benevolence there was no insipidity of character. A man must have been blind not to have perceived that beneath this placid exterior there was a vigorous and determined will. When principle came into play, no power on earth would have turned him an hair's breadth.

CHARLES DARWIN

THE kindly Reverend Professor John Stevens Henslow was truly a man of his time. As "distinguished naturalist and excellent man",[1] scientist, priest, magistrate, teacher, thinker and social reformer he sought to bring education—especially science education—to the people of all classes in his care. His upbringing and personality favoured him in this task which he undertook with imaginative zeal. His ingenious ventures are the subject of the following story which reveals the skills and timeless devotion with which Henslow succeeded in his task.

Professor John Stevens Henslow's life, 1796-1861, spanned a period of specific advance and rapid social change. Those who knew him as a child may well have predicted that he was destined to become an eminent and dedicated naturalist, they may even have seen that he would become a professor in his own field, but they could scarcely have imagined that Henslow would be teaching his beloved science, botany, with equal commitment to famous scholars such as Darwin, Berkeley and Babington at Cambridge, to the Royal children at the Palace, and to a volunteer class of village labourers' children in the overcrowded schoolroom he had provided for his Suffolk parish of Hitcham.

Henslow was born in Maidstone, Kent, on 6th February, 1796, the

9

son of a solicitor and grandson of Sir John Henslow, Surveyor and sometime Master of the Dockyard at Chatham. Living near the Medway, he spent many happy childhood hours collecting molluscs, insects and other natural history specimens with which he proudly returned home.[2] His father was himself an amateur naturalist with an aviary and a wealth of natural history material exhibited about the family house. No wonder young John, the eldest of eleven children, received much favour and was encouraged to follow his obvious scientific interests in an era when it was exceptional for young gentlemen to receive a scientific education.

At the age of nine John left his free mathematical school in Rochester to enter Dr Jephson's school at Camberwell as a boarder. By good fortune, the drawing master of the school was a keen entomologist and accompanied young Henslow on his natural history forays and instructed him in the art of setting and preserving insects. Later, so that John might follow his hobby more scientifically, the family engaged the services of a Dr Leach of the British Museum to teach the boy and introduce him to the Museum's collection. Leach, who had abandoned medicine for natural history, was currently cataloguing the crustacean collection and Henslow was able to assist in this interesting and absorbing task up till the time he left the school to become a student at St John's College, Cambridge in October 1814.

From these carefree beginnings as an amateur naturalist, John Stevens Henslow rose not only to scientific eminence but to become a successful pioneer in popularising scientific education among both adults and children alike.

There was no Natural Science Tripos at Cambridge University until 1851 so Henslow followed a mathematical course graduating as sixteenth wrangler in 1818. Only in his postgraduate years was he able to follow his burning scientific interests and at the early age of twenty-six was appointed to the Chair of Mineralogy and, but five years later, to the Regius Chair of Botany for the additional stipend of £200 a year.

Just as his childhood interests had been encouraged by a happy supportive home, so in adult life Henslow derived strength from his warm, Christian family circle. In the early years of his marriage to Harriet, daughter of the Reverend George Jenyns of Bottisham Hall, and while still resident in Cambridge as curate of St Mary the Less, Cambridge, Henslow's home was the friendly focus of scientific discussion among eminent men of the day. On Friday evenings friends and colleagues including William Whewell, mathematician and moral philosopher, and Adam Sedgwick, geologist, together with selected students met in the congenial atmosphere of the Henslow household and engaged in free and lively intellectual exchange. It was here at Henslow's soirees that Darwin first found the inspiration and stimulus that had heretofore eluded him in his undergraduate career, and it was to this welcoming and helpful household that he hastened with his specimens when returning from the voyage of the *Beagle*.

Further testimony to the peace and harmony of the family circle was given by Henslow's lifelong friend, Professor Adam Sedgwick, reflecting[3] on Cambridge summer days to Mrs Barnard (née Henslow) his goddaughter,

> "How different my life is from that it was in by-gone years when I used to run up to Parker's Piece and drink tea with your dear father and mother, and laugh and play with their children!"

The Reverend John Henslow continued to live in Cambridge even when appointed rector of Cholsey-cum-Moulsford, Berkshire, attending to his parish duties in the University vacations. Eventually, however, Henslow and family moved away from Cambridge to take up the Crown Living in Hitcham, Suffolk. Henslow confined his teaching duties in Cambridge to the summer term and spent the rest of the year in his new parish. Hitcham Rectory proved both a nerve-centre, from which he organised his energetic educational enterprises in the village and beyond, and a refuge and comfort in times of local strife and disappointment. The whole family contributed generously to his village charities and particularly to the village school. His son and daughter assisted with adult literacy classes and the elder daughter assisted her father in making illustrative material for his botany lessons at the school. The enterprising village excursions to the sea and elsewhere could never have succeeded but for the keen co-operation of Henslow's botanist son, George, and the younger daughter, Frances, later to marry the famous botanist, Joseph Hooker, himself a great admirer of Henslow. The parish farmers were not supportive of the rector's attempts to help the poorer classes and his eventual success was facilitated by the loyal assistance of his family and his scientific friends.*

Not only did the contributions of individual members of the family assist the professor in his endeavours but the close-knit Victorian family gave Henslow infinite happiness and serenity. His home was his workshop where lectures were prepared, examinations marked for Cambridge and London Universities, and specimens mounted for Ipswich Museum. Here, too, natural history specimens were collected. Eminent friends sent him most fascinating material which surrounded him at the rectory just as it had in his father's home. All visitors were shown the newest, fascinating acquisitions by their enthusiastic scientific pastor.

This caring and much-loved man made an exceptional contribution to popular scientific education in the Victorian era. While the reason for his success may lie partially in his undying enthusiasm for natural history, it also derives from his undoubted teaching ability, his commitment to practical measures for improving the lot of his parishioners, and particularly from a reconciliation of scientific methods and knowledge with an unshakeable personal Christian belief. He was, in fact, a man for his times, "at once the most popular and useful man of science of his day",[4] uniquely suited to the challenges of the mid-nineteenth century. This

*See Appendix I.

fitness for action is exhibited most dramatically against the backcloth of social conditions of the period.

The 1832 Reform Bill introducing universal male suffrage went through Parliament while Henslow was at Cambridge and there is little doubt that this and other related social reforms led to his involvement in the liberal awakening that captivated members of the intelligentsia at that time. His involvement in politics at Cambridge did not stem from personal ambition but from a distaste of wrongful actions and deceit. Thus it was that he allowed his name to be used in 1835 as the nominal complainant about the corrupt practice[5] of political bribery to out-of-town voters to bring them to the polls. His moral courage brought him considerable odium and the original inscription "Henslow Common Informer" could still be discerned on the corner of the wall of Corpus Christi College as late as 1955. Apart from campaigning for the abolition of religious tests for entry to Cambridge University, there is little evidence of further political involvement there. In Hitcham, he used the pulpit as a platform to campaign against excessive sentences for theft. The sermon[6] preached 20th March, 1842 "on the occasion of three persons of the parish being condemned to fifteen years transportation for sheep-stealing", was privately printed in Hadleigh and circulated as a tract to his friends and acquaintances. His challenge of the law derived from a strong sense of justice and he fulfilled his magisterial duties in the parish with renowned fairness and good humour.

Originally a Tory, Henslow became a follower of Palmerston, Member for the University of Cambridge, and Adam Sedgwick writes of the influence this political leader had on the young man's thinking. It is very likely that Henslow's appointment to the Crown Living of Hitcham was largely due to Palmerston's nomination, although the appointment was presented by Lord Melbourne, the Prime Minister at that time.

Of his many parish reforms, the improvement of agricultural practice appealed greatly to the botanist Henslow. Periods of agricultural distress, contributing eventually to the repeal of the Corn Laws in 1846, had brought great hardship to the English countryside and there was urgent need for reform in farming methods. The professor threw himself wholeheartedly into the movement to bring "practice with science" (the motto of the Royal Agricultural Society founded in 1838) to the English farmer. By correspondence in the *Bury and Norwich Post* in spring 1843 and in discussion with members of the local Farmers' Club at Hadleigh, he introduced that community to the use of modern chemical fertilizers and to the practice of good husbandry in an attempt to raise the efficiency of agriculture and to raise the standard of living of those who lived by it. To this end, too, he devised an allotment scheme for village labourers. This gave them insight into scientific care of crops as well as generally raising their morale. The men worked hard and competed enthusiastically for the prizes awarded by the Henslow family and their friends at the annual horticultural shows in the rectory grounds.

Technical advances had brought about their own revolutionary effects on communications on sea and land. In 1831, the *Beagle* set forth on a surveying expedition with Charles Darwin aboard. Indeed Henslow, who had long nursed a consuming and unfulfilled desire to explore the natural history of overseas lands, considered sailing on the *Beagle* himself. Family considerations prevented him from going and he recommended another scientist, Darwin his student, to accompany Captain Fitzroy on the voyage to South America and the Galapagos. The professor was certainly alive to the expanding world that improved communications had brought. The arrival of new flora and fauna from overseas were a challenge to him and his fellow systematists who swiftly realised the strain this imposed on the classification systems devised in the seventeenth and eighteenth centuries.

At home, the Stockton to Darlington train made its first journey in 1825 and the uniform Penny Post came into operation in 1840. Henslow's parishioners were very soon introduced to rail travel on their village excursions and the professor used the postal service to maintain contact with his village botanists by receiving their weekly exercises addressed to his Cambridge rooms during the summer term. While the villagers were no doubt marvelling at the wonders of these advances in communication, Henslow's letters constantly expressed his fury at their inefficiency and high cost!

John Stevens Henslow was ordained priest in the Church of England in 1824 at a time when advances of scientific knowledge and consequent technical developments were viewed with suspicion by the established church. Eminent scholars were concerning themselves with the resolution of this science v. religion controversy and a series of treatises were published between 1835 and 1840 as the result of a bequest by Lord Bridgewater for work on theistic apologetics. Two of these *Bridgewater Treatises* were written by close friends of Henslow's—William Whewell and William Kirby, a naturalist. Henslow's own philosophical stand was close to that of his friends and he saw the pursuit of science as providing a clearer insight into God's creation.[7] He never wavered from this position even when local critics questioned the propriety of his teaching science to village schoolchildren. He was deeply concerned that his pupils should be trained to observe critically and think scientifically, and these methods, which were undoubtedly a major contribution to botany teaching nationally, were to arouse suspicion and even hostility at parish level.

It is interesting that at the height of the science v. religion controversy, the professor calmly and ably chaired the famous, if bizarre, Huxley and Wilberforce debate arising from Darwin's *Origin of Species* at the British Association for the Advancement of Science meeting in Oxford in 1860. His open-mindedness and belief in the pursuit of scientific truth were respected by his science colleagues and afforded tacit support for his old pupil Darwin and his limited group of followers. It may well be significant, however, that the professor gained neither the same respect nor advancement in church circles as he did in scientific ones, in spite of his undoubted ability and sincerely-held Christian beliefs.

Other philosophical movements of the time were acknowledged by the professor: those working directly or indirectly for the cause of science education were embraced by him. For example, he associated himself with the Society for the Propagation of Useful Knowledge born of the utilitarian movement of the time. Universal suffrage implied to some thinkers universal education and supporters of this view, led by utilitarians John Stuart Mill and Jeremy Bentham, despised the classical curriculum of the day regarding it as irrelevant for most human endeavour. They sought to introduce more "useful" subjects. Political economy was particularly favoured and physiology had their approval. Indeed, the sciences were recognised by the S.P.U.K. as having a most acceptable place in the curriculum. Henslow, who worked devotedly to make education available to all his parishioners, ensured that his own personal teaching did not neglect the useful aspects of the subject. Economic applications of botanical knowledge were brought to the forefront of his lessons at all levels.

Natural history, of course, also had its aesthetic appeal which commended it to followers of the romantic movement of the times. The reverence of nature played a significant role in early nineteenth century thought. It was but a few years after Henslow's appointment at Hitcham that Wordsworth, himself educated at St John's College, Cambridge, and an eminent figure in the romantic movement, succeeded Southey as Poet Laureate. At this time, too, the Suffolk landscape painter, John Constable, was portraying the magic of the natural beauty of the countryside which Henslow came to know so well. Constable wrote

"the landscape painter must walk in the fields with an humble mind. No arrogant man was ever permitted to see nature in all her beauty"

The humble observation referred to by Constable here and captured in his enchanting East Anglian landscapes was not only regarded as a social virtue at the time but an ennobling human experience. Henslow readily agreed and encouraged all who would study nature carefully and never cease to wonder at its beauty.

CHAPTER TWO

A Cambridge Apprenticeship

JOHN Stevens Henslow's postgraduate years at Cambridge, first as Fellow of St John's College and later as Professor of Mineralogy and of Botany, can be regarded as a sophisticated apprenticeship to his subsequent work in popular science education. It was here, in his much-loved university that he developed his wide-ranging knowledge of the natural history sciences and his many gifts in communicating this knowledge to others. It was in the Cambridge world of scholarship and debate that he developed his understanding of and respect for scientific methods in the pursuit of truth and that he made close and lasting friendships with other eminent scientific men who encouraged him in his mission in later years.

Henslow graduated as Sixteenth Wrangler in 1818.[1] He had attended lectures on chemistry and mineralogy in addition to his mathematics during his undergraduate years but turned his attention to furthering his study of zoology immediately after graduating. He had followed the subject avidly as a schoolboy and his rooms in Cambridge were strewn with shells and insects collected in childhood and youth. Now he had time to add to his collection and organise it scientifically. Apparently he and his friend Leonard Jenyns[2] were the only two seriously interested in zoology at that time and spent much time together collecting in the neighbourhood. Some of their forays took place round Bottisham Hall—Jenyns' home. (It was here that Henslow met Jenyns' sister Harriet to whom he was happily married in 1823.) The zoological collection was finally organised and presented to the Cambridge Philosophical Society in 1820.

During this period, too, Henslow assisted Professor Cummings with chemistry demonstrations in the chemistry lecture room and so learned more of this science. Nor was it long before Professor Adam Sedgwick called on Henslow's help with work in geology. He assisted Sedgwick energetically with geological excursions and gave freely of his time and undoubted skill in helping to organise the Woodwardian Museum of Geology. His knowledge of geology developed greatly and the production of a geological map of the Isle of Anglesea as a result of a successful and careful survey by Henslow and some students gained him a high reputation among geologists.[3]

Professor Adam Sedgwick was greatly pleased with young Henslow's work and the two became firm friends, Sedgwick campaigned vigorously and successfully to get him appointed to the Chair of Mineralogy in 1822.

Henslow was then but twenty-six years old. The Heads of Colleges were opposed to new appointments to Chairs at this time as so many appointees had neglected their teaching duties. Henslow quickly justified his appointment and produced a *Syllabus* of lectures[4] which was a valuable systematic description of the mineral kingdom. This, his first lecturing assignment was a testing ground. He had not the eloquence of his predecessor but found he held his audiences with a clarity of exposition which he developed to the full in later years.

*   *   *

His career as a teacher as well as a scholar had now begun. There was another challenge soon to come. When the Professor of Botany died two years later, a compromise manoeuvre eventually enabled Henslow to take up the Regius Professorship of Botany without relinquishing his mineralogy post. For thirty years botany had lain fallow and no lectures had been given. Henslow was least familiar with this branch of science and so had to work hard to master yet a further aspect of natural history and to make the subject a viable one in the Cambridge scholastic scene.

The challenge was taken up enthusiastically. The young Professor Henslow turned his attention seriously to the skills of communicating his knowledge to others and of convincing them of its value.[5]

"He immediately arranged a course of lectures at once scientific, practical and popular, gave chemistry and physiology their legitimate places in botanical teaching and by applying his mathematical powers to giving a prominent place to geometrical problems involved in phyllotaxis, he awakened interest in a study to which some of the mathematicians had hitherto hardly accorded the dignity of science."

These classes attracted students and dons alike (even some ladies managed to slip in, so Jenyns reported), and numbered at one time near eighty people.[6] Henslow illustrated the lectures with his skilled, brightly-coloured drawings. He learned to involve his audiences and all attending were required to investigate floral specimens for themselves.[7]

"For this purpose he would provide the day before a large number of specimens of some more common plants, such as a primrose, and other species easily obtained and in flower at that season of the year, which the pupils, following their teacher during his explanation of their several parts, pulled to pieces for themselves. These living plants were placed in baskets on a side table in the lecture-room with a number of wooden plates and other requisites for dissecting them after a rough fashion, each student providing himself with what he wanted before taking his seat."

The practical exercises proved popular with the students and helped to hold their attention. But they had a more serious purpose of course—that of developing the art of scientific observation. His concentration on scientific investigation was a unique feature of his teaching and one which brought controversy when, as a priest, he introduced it later to his parish school. In this he was ahead of his time.

His botany lectures became an established part of the summer term programme and were advertised in February of each year. The 1830 notice[8] read as follows—

THE PROFESSOR OF BOTANY will commence his Course of LECTURES in the Museum of the Botanical Garden on Monday, April 26, at one o'clock.

Terms of attendance One Guinea.

N.B. The first two lectures will be occupied with introductory matter, afterwards the Lectures on Mondays, Wednesday, and Friday, will be devoted to the Physiological, and those on Tuesday and Thursday to the Demonstrative [later years changed to 'Descriptive'] departments of the Science—During the Course, three to four herborising excursions will be made, as the weather may permit.

Gentlemen willing to attend are requested to put down their names either at Messrs Deighton's or at Mr Stevenson's and the Medical Students will bring their cards to the Lecture Room.

Henslow spared himself no trouble in preparing his lectures and would have in the classroom on each occasion demonstration models and mountings of flower parts, herbarium illustrations and materials showing the useful applications of various plants. He was a firm believer in stressing the usefulness of science and later became associated with the Society for the Diffusion of Useful Knowledge. His future teaching incorporated utilitarian references and illustrations wherever they were seen to be appropriate. "Rotation of crops" was included under the Grasses and "economic fruits" under the heading Rosaceae.

There was much material to arrange for each botany lecture and he enlisted the help of students. Charles Babington, later to succeed Henslow as Professor, notes in his journal that having attended one of Henslow's lectures on 30th April, 1827, and talked to him after a second on 2nd May, he "Assisted Professor Henslow in putting his things in order before and after the lectures".[9] In addition to the illustrative materials already described, fresh material was always in evidence and this had to be collected and arranged for each class.[10]

". . . there were rows of small stone bottles containing specimens of all the British plants that could be procured in flower, the whole representing, as far as practicable, the different natural families properly named and arranged."

Henslow had indeed discovered that effective teaching was based on purposeful and thorough preparation and he maintained these high standards in his future and varied educational commitments.

It is interesting to reflect that Charles Babington, nicknamed "Beetles" Babington, had up to this point been devoted to entomology. He does not directly attribute his change of direction to Henslow's teaching but facts certainly suggest this was so. From this time on, Babington accompanied Henslow on many formal and informal field excursions, attended successive courses of botany lectures[11] and became generally involved in the botanical work of the university.

Another student, Charles Darwin, was more forthcoming in his appreciation of Henslow's lecturing technique. He recollected,[12]

"His [Henslow's] lectures on Botany were universally popular and as clear as daylight. So popular were they that several of the older members of the university attended successive courses."

He also commented[13]

"I attended Henslow's lectures and liked them much for their extreme clearness and the admirable illustrations."

The professor regarded lecturing, even with practical exercises, as but one means of conveying the nature of the subject and devoted considerable time and energy on organising field expeditions for his students and colleagues. It seems that entomologists, conchologists and geologists, as well as botanists joined Henslow on the excursions he organised two or three times a session. Darwin further recalled

"Henslow used to take his pupils, including several older members of the University, field excursions, on foot or in coaches to distant places, or in a barge down the river and lectured on the rarer plants and animals which were observed. The excursions were delightful."

One of Henslow's favourite excursions was to Gamlingay in the late spring to see the wild lily of the valley, and a variety of other species. It is clear that his students enjoyed these expeditions greatly and it is wistful reference to them made by Darwin in his letter from Rio de Plata,[14] in 1833,

"I trust I shall find a letter (although it is a long time to look forward to) at Valparaiso; I shall be glad to hear what you are doing—Very often during your last Spring when the weather has been fine, I have been guessing whether it would do for Gamlingay or whether at that very instant some reverend Botanist was not anxiously looking at the other side of a fenny ditch."

And Darwin's guesses were indeed correct. "One stage coach" of naturalists set forth that May for Gamlingay and Charles Babington was one of the party, possibly for the first of many occasions. He recorded that the Gamlingay visits continued until 1852 and that he accompanied at least nineteen of them. Alas when the party arrived in May, 1850, they found all the heaths "enclosed and most parts brought under cultivation".[15] Although the expedition "found the usual plants of the district" it was not long before a different area had to be explored by the Cambridge naturalists.

Henslow's wide-ranging knowledge of natural history was invaluable on the field outings and obviously an inspiration to Darwin[16] at the time.

> "He [Henslow] used to pause every now and then and lecture on some plant or other object; and something he could tell us on every insect, shell or fossil collected, for he had attended to every branch of natural history."

The popularity and effectiveness of these field excursions was obvious to Henslow and he later called upon his experience when organising floral forays for his Hitcham schoolchildren and general excursions for his village labourers.

* * *

The deliberate bringing together of people in congenial circumstances for their mutual enjoyment and education was yet another of Henslow's teaching tactics. His Cambridge field trips, for example, ended up with a meal for participants "in some inn or house" and, related Darwin, "most jovial we then were".[17] But a more sophisticated development was the institution of Henslow's Cambridge scientific soirees. These Friday evening "parties commenced on February 15th 1828 and were continued regularly during full term until the end of the year 1868",[18] attracting both famous men and students alike. They engaged in serious discourse in the welcoming surroundings of Henslow's home. Among those attending the soirees were Whewell (Professor of Moral Philosophy), Sedgwick (Professor of Geology), Sir J. Mackintosh (philosopher, historian and lawyer), the Reverend Mr Dawes (mathematician, later Dean of Hereford and another great promoter of popular science education) and Leonard Jenyns (botanist). Jenyns claimed that these events had an "immense importance in diffusing taste for science, no less than for inciting young men to intellectual pursuits". This is confirmed in an appraisal of the soirees by Darwin who soon organised himself "an invitation and went there regularly".[19] He reflected[20] that

> "when only a few were present I have listened to the great men of those days conversing on all sorts of subjects, with the most varied and brilliant powers. This was no small advantage to some of the younger men as it stimulated their mental activity and ambition."

Another successful student of Henslow's, the mycologist Mr Berkeley, told Jenyns[21]

> "I had the pleasure of being present at one or two of his *soirees,* which he continued to make extremely agreeable and interesting; and

he not only gave young men of scientific turn opportunities of beneficial intercourse, but he had especial meetings of more intimate friends for improvement in French."

So important a part of the scientific life of the university did those soirees become that, upon threat of their disappearance when Henslow took his Crown Living of Hitcham in 1837,[22] an adequate replacement was sought. The Ray Club was formed to fill the threatened gap. The club, named after the celebrated zoologist, John Ray, was instituted "for the cultivation of Natural Science by means of friendly intercourse and mutual instruction" so embodying the spirit of Henslow's original gatherings. Henslow's friend and colleague Adam Sedgwick was its first president and Babington took an active role from its inception.

In yet another teaching role, that of personal tutor, Henslow excelled. He had great natural gifts and clearly enjoyed this work which he deemed important. He gave time and attention to the young men in his care encouraging them in their own interests and stimulating them to further study.

A contemporary biographer[23] wrote of Henslow's encouraging manner with a student,

"he gave confidence in his earlier efforts, and led them on by example teaching and encouragement."

This theme of caring tutelage recurs in the warm *Recollections of J. S. Henslow*[24] written by Darwin later in his life. He recalled

". . . no man could be better found to win the active confidence of the young, and encourage them in their pursuits."
". . . he had a remarkable power of making the young feel completely at ease with him; though we were all awe-struck with the amount of his knowledge."
". . . all who cared for any branch of Natural History were equally encouraged by him. Nothing could be more simple or cordial and unpretending than the encouragement which he afforded."
". . . He would receive with interest the most trifling observation in any branch of natural history; and however absurd a blunder one might make, he pointed out clearly and kindly that one left him in no way disheartened, but only determined to be more accurate next time."

Lest these comments may be interpreted as the mellow indulgences of a successful scientist, it is healthy to note Darwin's on-the-spot comments on Henslow as tutor to a reluctant student. Writing to his friend W. D. Fox on 5th November 1830, Charles Darwin[25] admitted that he was not enamoured with the work at Cambridge—except for tutorials with Henslow!

"Reading makes me quite desperate, the plague of getting up all my subjects is next thing to intolerable. Henslow's my tutor, and a most admirable one he makes; the hour with him is the pleasantest in the whole day. I think he is quite the most perfect man I ever met with."

But Henslow was not uncritical nor indiscriminately supportive,[26]

"nor did he ignore the more practical duties as a teacher; no one knew so well as he did that to make botanists of students they must quickly be brought that in some directions at any rate they can and ought to walk unaided."

Charles Babington's *Journal* reveals that after initial and frequent botanical outings with Henslow from 1831, he was left to strike out further afield and investigate new habitats and new flora on his own initiative.[27] Darwin, too, was persuaded by Henslow to take "the position of naturalist on the *Beagle*"[28] and although Henslow advised Darwin on background reading—especially Lyell's new *Principles of Geology* which influenced Darwin's thinking so fundamentally—the young graduate was left to record and interpret his discoveries on his own supported merely by the distant approval and encouragement of his mentor in Cambridge.

* * *

During his days at Cambridge, Henslow arrived at his own philosophy of science and, for him, a clear understanding of its methods. To Henslow natural history was no idle hobby as ridiculed in Dicken's Mudfog Association.[29] It was a serious study involving observation and testing of evidence and was a vital approach to the pursuit of truth. When but newly graduated and on a geological tour of the Isle of Man with Sedgwick, in 1818, he agreed enthusiastically to help found a Cambridge Philosophical Society for senior members of the University interested in scientific debate. With Sedgwick as one of its first secretaries the Society was launched in November, 1819.[30] Its seriousness of purpose and published transactions have contributed much to the study of science within the university and beyond.

Professor Henslow was a friend of Dr Whewell, Professor of Moral Philosophy at Cambridge. Whewell was a frequent visitor at Henslow's home, especially to the Friday soirees where discussions on the nature of science—amongst other topics—took place. The two men undoubtedly influenced one another in their beliefs. Henslow always defended the importance of accurate and cumulative observation as a contribution towards the pursuit of truth. To this end he encouraged his botany pupils at Cambridge (and later in Hitcham) to observe critically and record accurately. His own scientific works were themselves models of scientific observation and objectivity. His successful *Geological Survey of the Isle of Angelsea* had already been mentioned but his early botany papers for the Cambridge Philosophical Society *On the Examination of a Hybrid*

Digitalis (1831) and *On the Monstrosity of the Common Mignonette* (1833) received fulsome praise from Dr Joseph Hooker who described them "of the highest merit as works of philosophical research",[31] and were prerunners of further work demanding accurate observation and "patient investigation"[32] on Henslow's part.

Generalisation, or the framing of working laws, derived from observed and established fact was recognised by the professor as a natural progression in scientific thinking and he accordingly encouraged his botanists to attempt a classification from observations made by them of flower structures. Further, he accepted that having built up a generalisation or working law the scientist could usefully employ it to assist future observations. The young botanists were thus enabled to identify the families (man-designated) to which newly found plants belonged and this was very important in an age when unknown flora was arriving from all over the world.

It was this interaction of deductive and inductive processes which had attracted Dr Whewell's interest in botany as an ideal science for general study. To Henslow's delight, Whewell strongly supported botanical science as an ideal one for inclusion in a liberal education.[33] His advocacy undoubtedly assisted in enhancing the position of botany in Cambridge and assisted entry of the subject into the reformed curricula of English Public Schools later in the century.

Henslow's own belief in the importance of objective scientific observation of natural phenomena in the pursuit of truth, and in the validity of establishing working laws based on verified facts, was tested in the fire of controversy which raged after his pupil Darwin published the *Origin of Species* in 1859.

Lady Barlow's sensitive editions of the correspondence between pupil Darwin and tutor Henslow[34]—extending as it does over the years, Darwin's selection for the *Beagle* voyage, the organisation and treatment of materials with the help of Henslow's friends, the publication of the findings and the subsequent acrimonious debate—emphasises the remarkably human story of Darwin's initial dependence on the inspiration and wisdom of the professor and of his eventual intellectual ascendancy over his "dear old Natural History Master"! Important in the present context is the unfailing respect Darwin's correspondence shows for the opinions of his Cambridge mentor. (Darwin always felt himself Henslow's pupil.) Reciprocally, Henslow showed Darwin a recognition of his outstanding scientific ability and intellectual integrity, and a loyalty to him and his work which was as courageous as it was unfailing. Even in Darwin's triumphant yet darkest hour, when contemporary scientists (including Henslow's friends Sedgwick and Owen) struck out bitterly at the threat posed by the Darwinian hypothesis of the origin of species and its implications for evolutionary theory. Henslow calmly restricted public debate where he could to the scientific considerations involved.[35] He never wavered in his support of his pupil's scientific integrity.

The professor had recognised, as early as 1835, that the descriptions sent to him from the *Beagle* journey were scientific observations of exceptional interest and merit and he took it upon himself to print a selection of the letters and present them as a paper to the Cambridge Philosophical Society on 16th November, 1835. Even here, Henslow craved caution in interpreting the facts presented by Darwin. He warned his audience and readers

> "The opinions here expressed must be here received in no other light than as the first thoughts that occur to a traveller rejecting what he sees before he has had time to collate his notes, and examine his collections with the attention necessary for scientific accuracy."

The members of the Society were greatly impressed by the extracts and it seems that Adam Sedgwick, who had previously assessed Darwin as a potentially idle man, was genuinely inspired by the observations made. Darwin recalls in his *Autobiography*[36] his surprise at the reactions of the scientific world.

> "Towards the close of our voyage I received a letter while at Ascension, in which my sister told me that Sedgwick had called my father and said I should take my place among the leading scientific men. I could not at the time understand how he could have learnt anything about my proceedings, but I heard (I believe afterwards) that Henslow had read some of the letters which I wrote him before the Philosophical Society at Cambridge."

But when eventually Darwin completed the organisation of his material, had carried out a number of experimental tests and had arrived at an interpretation of his data, Sedgwick and other members of the Cambridge Philosophical Society were no longer appreciative of Darwin's work. They contested not only the validity of the hypothesis but the method by which he had arrived at it.[37] Henslow drew the teeth of the Cambridge opposition as best he could by reaffirming his belief in the necessity of forming hypotheses as an inherent part of the scientific process. He chided them for being inconsistent—for accepting hypotheses in one field of science but not in another. In an extract from a letter he wrote to Joseph Hooker on 10th May, 1860[38] Henslow stated, describing the course of events,

> "Sedgwick's address last Monday was temperate enough for his usual mode of attack, but strong enough to cast a slur upon all who substitute hypotheses for strict inductions, and as he expressed himself in regard to some of C.D.'s suggestions as revolting to his own sense of right and wrong, and as Dr. Clark, who followed him, spoke so unnecessarily severely against Darwin's views, I got up, as Sedgwick had alluded to me, and stuck up for Darwin as well as I could, refusing to allow that he was guided by any but truthful motives, and declaring that he himself believed he was exalting and not debasing

our views of a Creator, in attributing to him a power of imposing laws on the Organic World by which to do his work, as effectually as his laws imposed on the inorganic had done it in the Mineral Kingdom.

I believe I succeeded in diminishing, if not entirely removing, the chances of Darwin's being prejudged by many who take their cue in such cases according to the views of those they suppose may know something of the matter. Yesterday at my lectures I alluded to the subject, and showed how frequently Naturalists were at fault in regarding as species, forms which had (in some cases) been shown to be varieties, and how legitimately Darwin had deduced his inferences from positive experiment. Indeed I had on Monday replied to a sneer (I don't mean from Sedgwick) at his pigeon results, by declaring that the case necessitated an appeal to such domestic experiments, and that this was the legitimate and best way of proceeding for the detection of those laws which we are endeavouring to discover.''

What then was Henslow's considered position in this important controversy? "Henslow,'' wrote Darwin to Asa Gray on the eve of publishing the *Origin*, "goes a very little way with me and is not shocked at me''. The professor himself later stated that he "cannot assent to his [Darwin's] speculations without seeing stronger proofs than he has yet produced.''[39] Even so he did not censure the scientist for attempting a hypothesis as did so many others, he cautiously admitted a proper, personal doubt about the validity (not the usefulness) of the hypothesis put forward by Darwin's explanation of the evidence to date. As he had told Hooker,[40]

"I do not disguise my own opinions that Darwin has pressed his hypothesis too far, but at the same time that his Book is (as Owen described it) the 'Book of the Day'.''

*   *   *

The professor's belief in the value of science in revealing God's truth was so strong that he seldom relaxed his efforts to further the cause of science both in the university and outside it. During these campaigns he evaluated his position in the science v. religion controversy which occupied men of learning of the day[41] and was convinced that the methods of science were essential in revealing the full extent of God's providence. He made these views known to theologians in Cambridge and elsewhere, especially when they were, in his view, obstructing the progress of science.

Even though his move to Hitcham diminished his influence on Senate after 1839, it was still considerable. As Professor of Botany he continued to give his Easter Term lectures and to encourage individual study of the subject amongst interested students. He regarded his own department's facilities as inadequate and legitimately campaigned to upgrade the Botanic Gardens. This campaign reached its peak in 1846 and Henslow not unnaturally linked it to a general call for the improved status of scientific study in the University. The movement to institute a Natural Science Tripos[42] had the Professor's unfailing support.

When he had been appointed to the Regius Chair in 1827 he had also been made Walker's Lecturer—a post elected by the Governors of the Botanic Garden. Although the lectureship brought no stipend, it entitled the professor to make use of the gardens. On his appointment he found the garden area confined and not of much scientific value. He had naturally reported their inadequacy to the Governors and, as early as 1831, he persuaded the University to purchase thirty acres of land on the outskirts of the town but no development took place at that time. The move to improve the status of science at the University had gained momentum and, in 1845, when Professor Whewell published his challenging *Address* on Cambridge Studies Henslow decided to press home the advantage while reviving his own call for action on the Botanic Gardens. Henslow's views were incorporated in an "Address to the members of the University of Cambridge on the expediency of improving and on the funds required for the remodelling and supporting the Botanic Gardens 1846."[43] This *Address* supported Whewell's appeal for a liberal education and advocated the full recognition of Natural History Sciences (including botany) within the University where they were not yet receiving equal recognition with mathematics and classics. It claimed that scientific botany could not now be taught adequately without an extended and remodelled botanic garden. Further, it called for a fund to be set up specifically for supporting and remodelling of the gardens. Henslow had consulted with Sir William Hooker of Kew and Professor John Lindley the previous year on the best way of bringing the gardens into line with those of Edinburgh, Glasgow and Dublin. On Hooker's advice he had already secured the services of a professional curator and a plan of development was ready at hand.

Henslow, having given utilitarian educational and philosophical arguments to Senate to justify Botanic Garden improvements, threw in for good measure a reference to the arrival of new plant species from overseas:—[44]

"The reason why a modern Botanic garden requires so much larger space than formerly, is chiefly owing to the vastly increased number of trees and shrubs that have been introduced within the last half century. The demands of modern science require as much attention to be paid to these, as to these herbaceous species which alone can form the staple collection in small establishments."

Which of these arguments eventually persuaded Senate to change its mind between spring and autumn of 1846 is not recorded. Nevertheless, Vice-Chancellor Tatham planted the first tree in the new site on 1st October of that same year! It was one of a belt of trees surrounding the grounds, planted with allied genera and species near one another. The remodelling went ahead and Henslow was well pleased with the new facilities, which were much used by members of the university engaged in scientific botanical studies. Moreover, the professor shared his pleasure with his Hitcham villagers as well as his Cambridge colleagues. One July day in 1854, over two hundred Hitcham inhabitants arrived by rail in Cambridge and toured the university—including the new Botanic Gardens[45]—with extensive plans in hand and Henslow and his younger colleague Babington as their guides.

In his successful campaign *Address* for remodelling the gardens the professor had seriously questioned the obstructive attitude of the conservative theologians at Cambridge towards science and its methods. In doing so he outlined those convictions which governed decisions and actions in much of his own educational work. First, he pointed to the limitations of the theologians' own methodology in pursuit of ultimate truth.

> "With whatever deference we may be prepared to look up to men who are deeply learned in verbal criticism, it is quite impossible for some of us (and I expect many of us) ever to believe that such persons can have caught the spirit of the scriptures, who will persist in couching their doctrines under such forms and in slothing their discipline with observances, which are ill adapted to encourage an intelligent people to advance in the observance of pure and undefiled religion."

Next, he reminded his readers that the natural sciences had added greatly to the knowledge of God's creation and therefore asked—

> "Has it not been chiefly owing to the progress of such sciences as have unravelled to us some portions of physical laws by which the works of creation have been advanced to their present condition, that so many misconceptions[?] have been successfully brushed aside which once entangled the best exertions of some of the foremost and devoted champions of the truth in former generations?"

He expressed the view that universities should encourage all branches of genuine learning:

> ". . . it may well be worthy of our consideration whether a University can safely cease from esteeming it a duty to encourage any department of sound learning which may assist in improving our general views of God's providence."

And, finally, he challenged the opposition by suggesting that universities were the right and proper places for debate on the quest and nature of truth. He asserted that this debate was neither meaningful nor even possible in a university where some branches of knowledge were omitted.

> "Where then might all unworthy notions about the results to which the Natural Sciences may yet conduct us, to meet with more decided contradiction and rebuke than within the walls of a University? and

yet how is this likely to happen again if the tendency to neglect these sciences shall continue to increase, as most certainly it has of late years been doing among us?"

So Henslow, having lent his weight to the campaign for the proper acceptance of science at Cambridge University, learned with delight in March, 1848, that the specially convened Cambridge Syndicate had suggested the introduction of both a Natural Science and a Moral Science Tripos. He was preparing an introductory lecture for Ipswich Museum at the time he received the joyful news, and it may well have confirmed his resolve to speak "On Natural History Sciences as a Branch of Study". He certainly utilised the hour and wrote a campaign passage into his Ipswich lecture.[46] Referring there to an alleged letter from a gentleman complaining about the all too partial education received at Oxford University, Henslow said to the provincial gathering and their scientific guests,

> "I fully agree with my scientific friend, that our Universities have been unduly negligent of the claims of science; but I am truly happy to find, from a printed communication just received, that an effort is being made at Cambridge in favour of adding some of the natural sciences to the hitherto exclusive system which has prevailed there. I am informed that a great deal of opposition is expected, but the attempt is considered worth making if it shall only show the world that there are persons in the University desirous of progress."

In the anticipation of the success of the Cambridge campaign, Professor Henslow had quickly prepared a syllabus for a pass examination in botany.[47] But his optimism had been too great on this occasion for the Cambridge Syndicate had been persuaded to delay their submission to allow Senate time for calm reflection. Reformers, Henslow included, were disgusted at the delay and having smelt victory took further action. A memorial was prepared in July for the Prime Minister. Henslow's was the only professorial signature but the remaining 223 included no lesser persons than Charles and Erasmus Darwin, Matthew Arnold, Thackeray, John Romilly and Charles Lyell.[48] Senate was jolted from complacency and the opposition collapsed by the beginning of the new academic year. In October it was agreed that every candidate for an ordinary degree, in addition to the studies formerly required of him, should attend lectures of one or two specified professors (among them Botany) and should pass an examination in the chosen subject(s). The next critical step was taken in 1851 when a Natural Science Tripos was at last instituted. It did not at first confer a degree by itself but the university was clearly taking science seriously. Henslow again responded to the improved climate for science teaching. He published *Questions*[49] to give students a better idea of the content of his course and, in 1853, re-edited his *Syllabus* for the pass-examinations. His botany students were increasing in number again.[50]

In 1860, Senate at last agreed that a student entering examinations for the Natural Science Tripos could be henceforth credited for his performance therein. So it was that in 1861, just before Henslow died, the first Honours papers were set in botany for the Tripos. The professor's son George recorded these events and concluded[51] with affection and satisfaction that,

> "the very last act of the Professor connected with the University before he died in that year [1861] was to examine the candidates for honours in this tripos in botany."

From 1837, when John Stevens Henslow was appointed rector for the Crown Living of Hitcham, the University of Cambridge found much of its professor's prodigious energies were now diverted to work in his Suffolk village. His country parishioners were soon to discover that their new priest was not only a sincere Christian and caring pastor but a tenacious and fearless reformer, an able and devoted scientist, and an experienced and effective educator who was to use his proven talents and missionary zeal to transform their way of life.

CHAPTER THREE

The Parish School and Other Charities

O F HITCHAM, 1837, Henslow's biographer wrote[1]

"With regard to food and clothing, and the means of observing the decencies of life, the inhabitants were far below the average scale of the peasant class in England."

Of Henslow, 1837, the Bishop of Ely testified[2] he was a man

". . . best calculated by his ability, activity and common sense to reform that populous, remote, and woefully neglected parish [Hitcham], where the duty of squire, magistrate and rector must all fall upon the latter."

Shortly before Henslow's arrival in Hitcham as Rector in 1837, the unemployment and social distress was so great that the poor rate averaged 27s per head of population, which was high for that period.[3] The challenge of this distressed parish was a real one and very soon the new rector embarked on social measures in keeping with the self-help philosophy of the times. Clubs encouraging thrift and careful household economy had been introduced into a number of England's parishes but not in Hitcham. He sought to remedy this and to educate the labouring families to value a more organised way of living.

The task was a daunting one. Glyde,[4] a local Suffolk historian, recorded in 1839, the ratio of criminals in the Cosford Union (in which Henslow's parish fell) to be the highest in the county, standing at 1 in 345 in the Hitcham population itself. Arson and crimes of violence headed the list of crimes in Suffolk's rural areas. Further, the vast majority of those persons coming to trial were labourers, although it is fascinating to read in the lists that innkeepers, blacksmiths, farmers, schoolmasters, one comedian (!) and one gentleman had not escaped the law that year.

As for the living conditions of these labourers, Glyde described the cottages as old ones, clay-walled, thatched and frequently undrained. All the family slept together. Their diet was restricted and barely adequate.

". . . with industry and frugality, their diet consists principally of bread and potatoes. There are, however, some who when their families are grown up, by putting their earnings together, occasionally get a piece of meat at their supper time and their Sunday dinner."

By 1841, however, the following self-help Clubs and Societies had been formed under Henslow's direction: coal clubs, children's clothing club (22 children enrolled), medical clubs (186 enrolled), wives' society, benefit society (16 enrolled), ploughing match society (22 members) and cricket club (23 members)![5]

These clubs depended largely on members' contributions for there was minimal help from farmers and landlords. Indeed, of the nearly £50 subscribed to Parish charities in 1841, £34 came from the Henslow family themselves. Furthermore, this £50 was not only shared between the charities listed above but also went to support the new parish school, the parish library and a church band.[6] It is abundantly clear that members' contributions were the vital element in upholding each club's finances. The enrolment and the accounting was simple enough. These are illustrated by the arrangements described for the Coal Club in Henslow's Parish Accounts, 1841. The aim of the club was to encourage self-help and more specifically to

"furnish the labouring poor with coals at the rate of 6d per bushel to resident parishioners and 8d a bushel to residents who were not parishioners . . . It is by means of such appropriation, by private subscription, and by the farmers consenting to cart the coals free of expense, that the poor will be able to avail themselves of the proposed benefit on the following conditions:

Parishioners to pay 6d and non-parishioners 8d weekly during the months of June, July, August and September until sixteen such subscriptions have been paid. Subscribers to receive 4 bushels in each month December, January, February and March."

The farmers gave little in the way of financial help to these initiatives but they did apparently agree to cart the coals free. Agree, that is, until Henslow upset them once too often by his charitable acts! The ploughing matches, so popular with the labourers and introduced early on Henslow's arrival at Hitcham, had caused bad enough feeling amongst the farmers who saw the energies of their employees being wasted on apparently non-productive tasks. But worse was to come. In 1845, Henslow attempted to bring in an allotment scheme. This brought vehement opposition. The farmers resented the energies of the men being employed for their own benefit. Reminiscing, Henslow's son George quoted an angry letter[7] received by his father from one of the farmers at that time,

"I am sorry to say that it appears that you [Henslow] are one of those philanthropical gentlemen who wish to make themselves popular with the lower class of society at the expense of the farmer; him you would crush and stamp underfoot if possible . . . In conclusion, I make this declaration, I will never cart another ton of coals for the poor so long as this sub-letting system is in existence."

The passionate opposition of these men made the rector's work extremely difficult in the early days. The farmers had harassed the former incumbent until they broke his spirit. Henslow was made of sterner stuff and, with the loyal backing of his family and a few friends, he tenaciously and tirelessly pursued these social reforms.

Glyde especially commended Henslow and also the Reverend Tighe Gregory for the outstanding work done in their respective Suffolk parishes in these difficult days. Charles Darwin, too, admired the progress made at Hitcham and sought information about the running of the benefit clubs from his old master to pass on to the Vicar at Downe, the Reverend Mr Innes, for like action.[8] He wrote in 1850

> "Down, Farnborough, Kent.
>
> I am extremely much obliged to you for your long letter on Benefit Clubs, which appear to me full of the *most* valuable suggestions. I have just sent it off to Mr. Innes.—Possibly either he or I may have to trouble you with a few further queries, but I hope not. The rules sent are considerably different from some of our adjoining clubs . . ."

and, in the margin of a letter[9] (in which, incidentally, he explains that he had personally administered chloroform to his wife on the birth of their seventh child!) he informed Henslow, in January 1850,

> "I am at work again and believe I have succeeded in persuading our Clodhoppers to be enrolled in a Club."

*   *   *

One of the most important of Henslow's initiatives was the founding of a parish school for the labouring classes. He campaigned for this charity more fervently than for any other and received little but abuse for his early efforts.

The only school provision available when Henslow came to Hitcham was that of a "wretched dame".[10] The professor himself, implied that she had "no knowledge of the art of teaching"[11] and was fully aware that it was patronised by children whom a local lady resident currently described as "better styled".

The problem of raising funds for a village school was a very difficult one, and Henslow, like many other clergymen in rural England found that he and his family had to bear the burden of the expense. He had a schoolroom built, on the opposite side of the road from the Dame School, engaged a teacher and opened the Hitcham Parish school in 1841 with a promise of subscriptions totalling only £6 12s 4d from eighteen parishioners. The remaining support came from his own family.[12] There was, of course, the expectation of children's pence from those attending school and a determination to enlist further help from his parishioners in due course.

The rector set to work to raise subscriptions but the cause of popular education was not well received by the wealthy of Hitcham who feared that by educating the masses they would get ideas beyond their station and thus upset the stability of existing society. Nevertheless, Henslow wisely confined the arguments in his appeal to those which were acceptable to the upper classes of the time, namely, the virtue of self-help and the reward of Christian charity. His first public appeal to the Christian charity was communicated to his parishioners in a letter dated 25th November 1841, introducing the statement of parish accounts.[13] The letter avoided an overtly personal plea by quoting from a general circular printed by the National Society for promoting the Education of the Poor in the Principles of the Established Church.[14] For good measure Henslow added a conscience-stirring exhortation from the book of Proverbs. The letter ran

> "I would more especially urge upon all parties the propriety of repelling a charge which was advanced last year in a circular which accompanied Her Majesty's Letter on behalf of the National Society viz:— that 'in too many instances it is quite disheartening to read the pitifulness of the sum that even extensive Parishes and wealthy neighbourhoods is all that can be raised, either to build a school, or to pay a teacher. Too many letters declare that Manufacturers give nothing; that Landlords give almost nothing; and that Farmers confine their bounty to the cartage of the materials'. He that hath pity on the poor lendeth unto the Lord; and look what he layeth out, it shall be paid him again. Proverbs 19. I remain, faithfully and sincerely yours, J. S. Henslow."

The circulation of Henslow's composite letter of appeal, may have stirred a few consciences for the number of subscriptions rose from 18 to 24 in the next financial year. There were 40 children enrolled at the school and the School Accounts for 1842/3 looked healthier:

		£	s.	d.
Receipts —	Balance from 1841		19	0
	Subscriptions	13	1	6
	Children's pence	12	3	5
	Total	26	3	11
Payments —	J. Stowe (4 quarters)	16	0	0
	T. Lister (4 quarters)	1	0	0
	Rewards (in part)	2	0	0
	Incidental expenses	1	15	0½
	Balance	5	8	10½
	Total	26	3	11

Among these early subscribers were a Sir James Brodie, London surgeon, Ransome, a member of the famous Ipswich engineering firm, and a number of villagers—Luckey, Ennals (coal merchant), Pilgrim (farmer)

(i) John Stevens Henslow from a portrait by T. H. Maguire. *Ipswich Record Office*

(ii)   Frances Harriet Hooker (née Henslow).

Reproduced by permission of Oliver Hooker: Print lent by Mea Allan

(iii)   Joseph Dalton Hooker.   *Linnean Society*

(iv)   Charles Darwin.

Linnean Society

(v) Charles Cardale Babington.

(vi) John Stevens Henslow—marble bust by F. Woolnerin, Cambridge Botany Department.

(vii) Bottisham Hall near Cambridge, home of Henslow's wife, Harriet Henslow, née Jenyns.

(viii) St John's College, Cambridge.

(ix) "Henslow Common Informer". An inscription made in 1835 on the wall of Corpus Christi College, Cambridge, and still visible in 1955. *Richard Burn*

included—whose children gained merit at the school in subsequent years.[15]

In spite of the improving situation the major support still came from the rector and his family. Of the above subscriptions the Henslow family gave £4 3s 0d in addition to paying for the general upkeep of the school and the employment of the schoolmistress. No wonder Henslow was so incensed by the vandalism that had taken place. The "incidental expenses" figures above related to wear and tear which were, as Henslow recorded[16] with disgust,

> "partly occasioned by wanton mischief the perpetuators of which do not reflect that they have been robbing the poor of money which might have been better employed than in repairing such injuries."

While the number of subscribers was up again in the following year the total receipts were down and Henslow prepared himself for a new campaign to raise funds for the school which now totalled 90 pupils. On this occasion he chose to preach directly to the farmers and other influential parishioners who attended his church on the second Sunday of January, 1843. For these good people he introduced strong social as well as moral arguments to support his cause. Lest any with the means of help should have been absent from the church that day, or perhaps had not concentrated on the nature of the appeal, he had the sermon printed and circulated.[17] He obviously presented his cause with sincerity and fervour and a measure of impatience is discernible as he states.

> "I say that in general, I should never wish to see you give alms for any other reason but for Christ's sake; and yet in the case of the school, I am bold enough to ask those who differ with me, to yield to my judgement. For I feel myself much better qualified to judge of the important duty of our educating the poor than anyone of you . . ."

The sermon goes on to outline urgent social and economic reasons for popular education. It reads less like a country sermon than a counter to Cobbett—the man of the people who surprisingly opposed the government's proposal to finance education of the poor, in 1833, by arguing in Parliament that a ploughman was not made a better ploughman for receiving education. In contrast, Henslow's sermon proceeded—

> "There is no doubt that an ignorant man may execute the laborious work which may be required of him, quite as well as if he were well educated. But, rearing a human being without attention to the cultivation of his mind and morals you leave him only in the helplessness of his natural instincts, instead of filling him with the resources of an improved intelligence and the possession of the right understanding of his duty to God and Man. See the consequences now before you. A day of trial has arrived, in which you giving him no employment of the only kind to which the straightened use of his best faculties has been directed, is utterly powerless to help himself. He is

at once a burden on the community and a thorn in your sides. The inhumanity (as it appears to me) to say nothing of the impolicy of showing no care for the education of the poor, is in direct opposition to the spirit of the gospel."

As in other rural areas at that time, the unemployment of the agricultural labourer mentioned in the sermon was the underlying cause of most social problems in the parish of Hitcham. Henslow had tried to persuade some of the able-bodied young men to go to the north of England where industrial employment was now available. This did not prove acceptable.[18] He later tried to tackle the problem directly through the provision of allotments for labourers to work and grow food for their families. In fact, the national social problems outlined in Henslow's sermon remained so acute in the village of Hitcham that the congregation could not have failed to understand the very pressing meaning of his words even if they did not applaud this further attempt at a solution—popular education of the poor.

The sermon next outlined the elementary work so far accomplished in the school of two years standing. The schoolmistress's efforts had been devoted, it appears, to teaching children to read and write with tolerable facility. Henslow expressed his belief[19] that by such education

"we should be rearing a more intelligent, industrious and more provident people than our own times can boast of."

Finally, he roundly attacked those who, concerned for the "eternal welfare of the poor", see no cause to educate them in earthly matters.

"It may be perfectly true that their being able to read and write is not necessary to their salvation, but still education is an important accessory, a powerful ally, to them that are saved; and it may have been the very means of pointing out to the sinner the error of his ways, and of enabling him to turn to the only 'name under heaven, given among men whereby he must be saved.' *Acts 4.12.*"

Thus he enjoined the Christians in his flock who were still doubtful on this issue of popular education "to be turned and strengthened" in the belief "that the soul be without knowledge, it is not good. *Proverbs 19.2*". A declaration which, admitted the rector, came from "a higher authority than my own opinion".

In spite of these powerful exhortations there was no material improvement in the provision of funds the following year. Only three incomes from the Sparrow Charity helped swell the receipts for 1844 a little.[20]

Inside the bell tower of Hitcham's Church there is a plaque referring to two old Hitcham Charities—the Sparrow Charity and the Feoffment Charities. The former was a specifically educational charity described in White's Directory of Suffolk thus,

"In 1714, Benjamin Sparrow left a yearly rent charge of 18s out of lands now belonging to the Reverend I. Wallis, for schooling two poor children."

The plaque in the bell tower more specifically states that the Sparrow Bequest was for teaching two poor children to read. It is unclear how the money had been used before Henslow came but suffice to say that he early and successfully channelled the Sparrow money into the school funds. Use of the Feoffment Charities was a later episode in the economic progress of the school.

The rest of the story is told in the carefully kept Parish Accounts. These were submitted annually according to the rector's expressed proposal from the pulpit, 1st January, 1843.[21]

"I shall therefore propose to you at once, that the Saturday between Good Friday and Easter Sunday of every year, be the day on which we assemble at 11 o'clock in the Parish School, to consider the details and to audit the accounts of our Systematic Charities."

From these annual audits it is clear that the burden continued to remain with the Henslow family for the next decade.

*   *   *

Income from the children's pence fluctuated from year to year with a chiefly downward trend. This was most probably due owing to the irregular attendance of the older children and was a common problem throughout the land with Suffolk certainly no exception. The Reverend Mr Mitchell, Inspector of Schools, comments in his reports[22] that two of the main difficulties affecting the schools in the neighbouring towns and villages of Hadleigh, Bentley, Bury, Sudbury and Bildeston were the early leaving age and fluctuation of scholars.

Glyde described children's work on the Suffolk farms at the time.[23] In some districts six year olds were at work.

"Boys sometimes come at 2d a day; little things that can hardly walk come with their fathers. More usually nine- and ten-year olds boys would be weeding, corn dropping, pulling turnips, 'crow-keeping', 'stonepicking' and carting for 1s a week. Girls were largely employed 'stonepicking' and 'keeping birds'. The older girls would absent themselves from school for 6-8 months of the year to earn 6d a day."

The professor's struggle to maintain the school was exacerbated by increasing costs. As it was, the schoolmistress was paid but £18 per year compared with the average of £33 for the county.[24] A promise of help from the National Society must have been greatly welcomed. In 1853, the government voted annual grants for the support of schools in the agricultural districts at the rate of 5s for boys and 4s for girls in schools with between 15 and 100 scholars. The future of Hitcham School certainly looked more hopeful.

Before qualifying for a grant, however, each scholar must have attended 192 days of the year and not less than 1d and not more than 4d have been paid on his account. Further, the school had to show the income from subscriptions of 14s for every boy and 12s for every girl at the school. The 1852 accounts showed that Henslow had barely a quarter the required amount in subscriptions[25] but Henslow did not make another impassioned appeal to his parishioners. Instead, Henslow's family once more came forward to meet the challenge and their contributions undoubtedly ensured the school's eligibility for its share of the government grant.

The National Society had obviously accepted Henslow's grant application at once and with the extra money,[26] there came certain conditions to be honoured. The school was required to appoint a certificated teacher. Henslow sought the help of his ex-colleague Dawes, now Dean of Hereford, who was also deeply interested in popular education including science for schoolchildren. No immediate solution was available as the Dean's letter[27] of 1853 explains,

> "There is no-one to whom I would so soon send one of my protegees among my schoolmistresses as soon as yourself but I really do not know one who is at liberty. There is one very promising young woman of about 22 whom I brought to this county about two years ago and she was doing well—four months ago she was obliged to give up her instruction on account of health."

Dawes therefore suggests that Henslow contacts the Home and Colonial and Whitelands Colleges and in a later letter gives the names of contacts. Eventually, a properly qualified mistress was appointed to Hitcham's parish school in 1854. Miss Richardson took up her appointment and Henslow rejoiced at the general improvements that the remodelling had brought about under this "accomplished and efficient teacher".[28] The number of children now stood at over 80 and, like other schools at the time, the burden of the teacher was eased by reintroduction of the monitorial system whereby the older, successful children were put to teach the younger. Parents complained about this aspect of reorganisation as Henslow revealed in his School Report.[29]

> "But says Mr. Knowlittle, I want to have the schoolmistress teach my child herself, and not to set a monitor over her, to hear her lessons."

Henslow pointed out, with devastating candour, that with eighty pupils to teach the schoolmistress could only give but four minutes of her time each day to an individual pupil. If she were to divide her time equally between them it would be a hopeless situation. Further, he replied that the senior pupils were well educated—better educated than some of the parents raising the objection! With acceptance of the grant there also came the annual examination in prescribed subjects. Thus a minimum syllabus was laid down. In addition to the reading and writing which, until now had been the main concern of the school, the simple processes of arithmetic were to have equal place for the younger children. Pupils over eleven were required to study not only compound rules of arithmetic and learn grammar, but to take geography and other subjects of useful information. From 1852, Henslow had himself been teaching botany to a volunteer class of his village schoolchildren on Monday afternoons in the autumn and spring terms. So important did this innovation in science teaching become that it won Hitcham school a position of national esteem.[30]

The school ran effectively on its new lines for several years and Her Majesty's Inspectors adjudged it suitable for the apprenticeship of pupil-teachers in 1856. The pupil-teacher system which had been inaugurated officially 11 years before this, enabled pupils of 13 years of age or more to receive at least 1½ hours further instruction a day before or after assisting with the teaching in a school. Their apprenticeship, only possible in efficient schools, lasted five years and attracted a government remuneration of £10 the first year, increasing by £2 10s 0d each succeeding year if the required examinations were passed. The government paid their stipend and an extra allowance was given to the schoolmistress. A Minute issued by the Committee of Council on Education in 1845 had invited managers of schools to make applications to their lordships in Privy Council to apprentice efficient scholars. Inspectors would then report on the efficiency of the school so that an informed decision could be reached. Clearly, their lordships had approved Hitcham Parish School in 1856 as efficient and worthy to receive apprentices and the following year Harriet Sewell, herself a product of the school and a prize-winner in Henslow's botany classes, became its first pupil-teacher.

Henslow was very interested in the scheme and was personally concerned for the progress of these youngsters involved. As early as 22nd July 1856, the prospective pupil-teacher had to sit an external examination. On Thursday 24th June, Henslow was writing to his good friend Curator Knights about museum matters and told him that he would be in Ipswich on 22nd July escorting "a schoolmistress and pupil candidate".[31] The selected scholar, Harriet, had to prove her worth at an external examination there. This initial examination was nearly of the 5th standard and, if passed successfully, led to preparation for an annual examination of a yet higher standard. A successful pupil-teacher would earn the annual increments if the apprenticeship were to continue normally. Thus, in the following July, when Henslow wrote Knights a long letter concerning purchases for Ipswich Museum, he explained that he would be in Ipswich that month anyway as he must come over on the 29th to a further pupil-teacher examination.[32] The candidate, Harriet Sewell, was undoubtedly successful at the examinations for she not only remained apprenticed to the school but the Parish Accounts show that her stipend thenceforth increased regularly.

She was to be joined two years later by Marianne Baker, another of Henslow's volunteer botanists. The appointment was permitted even though the Inspector's annual report on the school was less favourable that year than previously. The schoolmistress's illhealth had evidently led to a decline in discipline but 1859 had nevertheless proved a successful year academically. Not only did Marianne become the school's second pupil-teacher[33] but her sister Susan Baker received a Government Scholar's certificate for attendance and proficiency and gained a place at the Normal Training School. The same certificate was awarded to Maria Gosling at Hitcham school and she, together with another classmate, was appointed pupil-teacher at Eye.[34]

Professor Henslow delighted in the success of these young scholars but it is clear that he was less concerned about producing teachers than that his pupils should receive a liberal education. He admitted in his 1859 School Report that it did not matter whether they became teachers or not and added

"It would be a great mistake to suppose that educational training of the mental powers should be restricted to merely professional prospects; and it is encouraging to see Pupil-Teachers undergoing their yearly examinations in a variety of subjects, as I have seen them in Ipswich."

Not surprisingly botany and arithmetic were singled out by him as subjects of particular educational value.

*   *   *

It is well to reflect that when Her Majesty's Inspectors looked at a school applying for apprentice pupil-teachers they enquired not only about the qualifications and competence of the supervising teacher, the organisation, disciplining and furnishing of the school, but, as one might expect, about the probability of permanent financial support. It was almost entirely due to the rector's endless generosity that the school was properly funded and progress was maintained.

The financial burden was indeed heavy and Henslow clearly had no money to spare for good causes outside his own parish. As a measure of self defence he had, in 1856, the following *cri de coeur*[35] printed at the head of his notepaper,

"Memorandum. Application for pecuniary aid towards the multiplicity of objects more or less interesting, continually arrived by post. Applications for information involving more or less scientific detail are yet more frequent. Now, this Parish is not half awake to vital importance of educating its population. The poor are unable, and the rate payers do not advance the funds necessary to meet sine qua non requirements of the government for school building, furnishing etc. The responsibility of the school efficiency rests on my shoulders, this and other parish necessities often oblige me, very unwillingly to decline attention to a large proportion of applications of the first description referred to above. In regard to the second description, I beg today to all who are not personal friends and acquaintances that I am willing as heretofore to attend to their wishes; but in return I shall be glad that whenever they regard my information worth anything, that they will send a contribution (perhaps a few stamps) towards our Parish school fund. J. S. Henslow."

The memorandum indicates clearly that the Inspectors were not fully satisfied with the size and furnishings of the school. To improve it meant the acquisition of a substantial amount of money before the Society would match it with a grant in aid. Henslow had to seek assistance elsewhere.

There existed in Hitcham, as can still be seen on the plaque in the church's bell tower, an ancient charitable trust, the Feoffment Estate vested in trustees of the poor of the parish. This was not primarily an educational trust as was the case of the Sparrow charity. A government Act of 1841 to afford further facilities with conveyance and endowment of sites for schools, enabled trusts like the Feoffment trust to be used as a vehicle for extending educational facilities for the poor. Robert Ennals, a Hadleigh coal merchant and regular subscriber to the school charity was the treasurer to the Feoffment Trustees. He wrote to all trustees on 11th April 1957,[36] calling them together in the schoolroom,

"for the purpose of considering the propriety of conveying the site of the Parish School House and Coal House attached thereto, and the Garden Ground contiguous to the adjoining Cottages, to Trustees, for the benefit of the paid School, under and by virtue of Statute passed in the 5th year of the reign of Queen Victoria, . . ."

Nothing of the debate is recorded but there is a simple statement of resolve in the Feoffment charity record book, dated 17th April 1857, which records the resolution "that the site of the school be conveyed for Educational purposes".[37] Given the site, Henslow proceeded directly to the erection of that extra classroom. The cost is revealed in the school accounts for the year 1857-58 which are entered in full here so that comparisons may be made with earlier years and the growth and extent of the enterprise assessed.

Most Government grants available to voluntary schools had to be matched in some measure by volunatry subscriptions. This was even true of the grant for maps and books listed in this account. As much as two thirds of their cost had to be subscribed voluntarily. For buildings, half the cost had to be raised in subscriptions. For this particular year the Henslow Family donations amounted to £11 of the £53 19s 0d shown and there was an additional donation of £20 from Henslow himself! The family's generous provision allowed the work of extending the school to go forward while the government repaid £80 of the money for the new classroom in the following year.

		£	s.	d.
Receipts	Subscriptions	53	19	0
	Government capitation grants	8	10	0
	Government grant			
	a. To Schoolmistress	10	0	0
	b. To Pupil Teacher	10	0	0
	c. Maps and books	2	1	3
	Children's pence 1st quarter	5	2	4
	2nd quarter	5	1	8
	3rd quarter	5	13	11
	4th quarter	4	2	0
	Sparrows charity (2 years)	1	16	0
	by Messrs. Ransome, Ipswich[38]	1	3	6
	Balance due to J.S.H.	132	1	9
	Total	239	11	5

		£	s.	d.
	Balance	10	12	0
Payments	Schoolmistress	40	0	0
	Rent of house	5	0	0
	Government grants to Schoolmistress			
	and pupil teacher	20	0	0
	Incidental school expenses	3	19	2½
	Towards prizes	3	17	10½
	Carpenter	80	2	8
	Bricklayer	40	17	1
Extension	Glazier	11	3	9
	Blacksmith		6	7
costs	Stove	3	5	0
	Iron rails	10	13	0
	Legal expenses (in part) for conveying	7	10	3
	Coal (2 tons)	2	4	0
	Total	239	11	5

N.B. The school is indebted to Mr. Ennals for gratuitously
carting from Hadleigh the coals required.

The income from children's pence had greatly increased. In spite of the
fact that there were now only 80 children attending the school, they were
attending more regularly. According to the 1859 records, 73 of these
qualified for a grant by virtue of their attendance and regular payments.
Henslow had adopted a new method of obtaining the weekly pennies in
advance now. The wording on the ticket[39] issued to a paid-up pupil runs—

Nomination ticket
To Hitcham Parish School for 1859

This ticket guarantees the payment of 4/- for the
current year towards the education of

Hannah Reynolds

on condition she also pays 1/- quarterly and complies
with the rules of the school.

signed   *W. SMITH*

If the child admitted by this ticket is to be excused
at the Church Sunday school, the subscribers must
state this below; otherwise the child will be required to
attend.

This child may be excused of attending the Church
Sunday School.

Although there is no record of Mr Smith nor who he was, nor his
relationship with the child Hannah Reynolds, it was likely that the persons
named on the specimen ticket were employer and child of employee. It was
now quite common for an employer of labour to contribute a sum equal in
school pence of families employed by him, or for owners and occupiers to
contribute according to the number of children attending schools from
cottages on their respective lands.

Gradually, Henslow had built up an effective parish school with a
predictable income and a sound financial base. The founding and
successful development of the institution were due almost entirely to the
professor's generosity and determination. From the outset he had accepted
that the school was the most important of the parish charities and worthy
of every support his family could give it. From Hitcham pulpit he declared
in a sermon on Parish charities, January 1844, "I always considered our
school to rank foremost in the list and certainly it is far the most important
of them."[40] But his interest was as much in the quality of education that
went on within the walls as in the provision of the facilities themselves.
Daily he contacted the youngsters as they came out of class and kept in
touch with the work in progress. It must have been most gratifying to him
to know that within twenty years of his arrival in a depressed, degraded
parish this little school was providing more than its share of pupil-teachers
in the neighbourhood. Further, his own involvement in the teaching made
this modest school unique. His Monday botany lessons to a volunteer class
attracted the admiration of the Inspectorate and other influential men. In
teaching science to so young a group, Henslow was ahead of his time and
his achievements focussed national attention on this small and struggling
parish school.

CHAPTER FOUR

Botany Teaching in a Village School

FROM the school's foundation, in 1841, the professor had taken a personal interest in the teaching at the parish school. Apparently, he kept in daily touch with the progress of work by talking to the pupils on their way home from school in the afternoons. It is currently claimed by members of long-established families still resident in Hitcham village that Henslow would wander past the school each day as the children came out. His pockets were filled with sweetmeats which he would distribute to the pupils as he listened to their chatter.

Eventually, he decided to involve himself actively in the teaching and, in 1852, when the school was firmly established he introduced his beloved botany as a subject for selected pupils. A volunteer class was inaugurated and held on Monday afternoons for some of the older children.[1] It was very popular with the pupils and the class not only maintained a good attendance but grew to a size limited solely by the room available. The professor's move to introduce a science was, however, an unusual one for the elementary schools of Victorian Britain and brought him considerable notoriety. His contemporary at Cambridge, Dean Dawes of Hereford, also gained nation-wide attention by introducing both natural history and technology into Kings Somborne School, Dorset. Here, it is recorded, the classroom was strewn with natural history objects. Dawes, however, seems to have avoided the emphasis on scientific thinking which was to prove the controversial issue in Henslow's teaching at Hitcham.

These local initiatives came, coincidentally, when the need for scientific education in Great Britain had been brought to government's notice on the occasion of the Great Exhibition at the Crystal Palace in 1851. The advance of other European countries in scientific education had been made very obvious and gave impetus to the formation of the Department of Arts (1852), and of Science (1853), under the Board of Trade. Compared with subsequent official developments in science education, Henslow's village botany classes appear as a very humble innovation. Yet they were to take a disproportionate part in the national movement to bring science to the schools of this country. Prince Albert, himself, sought Henslow's services to introduce botany to the Royal children in 1860.

While the professor's botany teaching was to gain fame and favour far beyond Hitcham's parish boundaries it was, alas, to cause considerable bitterness within them. It was not the subject matter itself which gained such favour on the one hand and discredit on the other but rather the methods of thought encouraged by Henslow, the scientist, amongst his pupils. He intentionally aimed at developing habits of observation and scientific thinking amongst his village youngsters. And, it must be remembered, that these exercises took place when the methods of science were seen as a challenge and potential danger to established society. It seemed to some that science could, in the long term, well destroy existing traditions and beliefs. Perhaps it was because of the Hitcham rector's own unshakeable Christian beliefs and his acceptance that any new discoveries could but add to the knowledge of God's world that made him less assailable as a science teacher. Perhaps, also, it was the socially un-controversial nature of the subject matter of botany in those days that made the subject less vulnerable to attack than physiology and other sciences offered to the schools.[2] Whatever the reasons for the eventual and successful establishment of botany as a school subject, the result was not achieved without acrimony.

Reflecting now on the delightful Monday afternoon lessons at the parish school at Hitcham, it is difficult to appreciate their provocative quality. It is easy to imagine the enthusiasm of the young botanists (ages ranged from eight to eighteen!) each armed with a needle, penknife and handlens, bent over dissecting boards and diligently investigating the structure of the flowers provided for them. The parts of the flower were removed, identified and counted by each individual and recorded in the printed schedules[3] prepared by Henslow himself. The recorded facts formed the basis from which more general truths were drawn about the characteristics of flowers belonging to that particular Order of plants. In short, an understanding of the "Natural System" of plants was derived in part from the pupils' own observations. It was this simple, first-hand scientific investigation which commended the teaching method to scientists of the day but gave greatest provocation to Henslow's critics.

For those pupils who succeeded in these scientific exercises, the reward must have lain in both the process and the achievement. But, Henslow was too shrewd a pedagogue to expect every child to be equally motivated by the work process alone. He thus arranged a system of extensive awards.[3] Standard prizes were clearly set out in the printed schedule* given to each pupil and it will be seen that they relate to further work in study of botany.

> "Rewards for proficiency—Promotion from third to second class, lens and forceps. From the second division to the first division, a vasculum, glue-pot and stand, paper-drying rack, book; those in the first division are entitled to prepare dried specimens and contend for prizes."

Some of the individual prizes for the first division were given by Henslow's friends and relations and a few extra prizes were introduced by the professor himself and he clearly enjoyed awarding them. For example, he shares his sense of fun with Knights of Ipswich Museum when he wrote[4] thanking him for buying these prizes,

*At end of Chapter Four.

"I quite forgot to thank you for the cigars. They will make interesting prizes, as I find they are needlecases. I put one in my mouth at school, and looked very sober, as if I were smoking, to the great surprise of Miss Richardson (the school mistress) and the children who stared at me as if they thought I had lost my wits."

At the end of a Monday class, Henslow would give a lecture introducing a broader view of the Order already investigated practically by the individual pupils. He prepared magnificent botanical drawings for his lectures (these were later copied for the Department of Science and Art) and he used material from the school herbarium to show related local species. Further, he secured what materials he could to show the economic properties, geographical distribution and historical relations of any particular species or genera in the orders.

In the lecture part of his afternoon's teaching he always introduced useful information about the plants concerned. This was the era of Utilitarian philosophy epitomised in the writings of Jeremy Bentham and John Stuart Mill; society of the time questioned the usefulness of established education—especially the grammar schools' traditional classical syllabus—and the Society for the Diffusion of Useful Knowledge flourished. The professor was certainly in sympathy with this movement but it is highly likely the inclusion of useful applications in his teaching was partly a pedagogical decision. He clearly saw the importance of evoking the relevance of the subject matter to capture the attention of students whatever their age or ability.

Something of the range of useful knowledge given to the school village botanists can be deduced from the manuscript Henslow was preparing for a textbook for beginners. The unpublished manuscript was the basis of Part II of Professor Oliver's *Lessons in Elementary Botany*, 1864, which embodies the scientific approach to systematic botany. Oliver, in his preface, explains that he has omitted much of Henslow's economic botany from the final textbook but gives examples of the discarded material. Thus we learn that the Henslow manuscript featured "an account of soap-making, and the method of ascertaining specific gravities, in connection with the Olive order represented in Britain by the Ash". Reference had similarly been made to "glass making under Saltworts, formerly burnt for the sake of their alkaline salts", "brewing under hops".

In addition to the interest thus fostered by these economic uses of plants, Henslow deliberately highlighted any gastronomic uses for the Order under study and illustrated them by a *bonne bouche*. He knew this was a sure way of imprinting the group on a child's mind. Thus we read that at the close of the lecture he collected any plant-list schedules that had been prepared over the week and anyone who produced the minimum required of him received a reward in the form of "some little gastronomic illustration (such as rose lozenges, to represent Rosanths, olives, the order Oleanths etc.) of the economic properties of the orders of the day".[5] The presentation was undoubtedly a popular conclusion to the lesson and Henslow made considerable efforts to acquire appropriate material. His long-suffering colleague Knights of Ipswich was required to go shopping. Henslow wrote,[6] 7th September 1855,

"I have promised my botanical school children some angelica as a botanical sweetmeat; would you be so kind as to procure me about 2/6d worth and either send it to me or bring it with you on the 19th?"

Or again, when Henslow was approaching a study of the Umbellifers three years later, Knights was prevailed upon to buy some "Caraway Comfits".[7] The request for 1s 6d worth was an urgent one and the purchase to be of an exact kind—"the kind in which the Caraway is only just coated with sugar". On 15th December 1858, eight days later the success story is told in a letter,[8]

". . . the things came safely to hand, and the results were satisfactory to the Village Botanists, who were able to taste the dish of 'Pippins and Caraways' alias 'baked apples and Caraway Comfits' in illustration of the order of Umbellifers (Cowparsley etc.) at Monday's lecture."

No wonder Henslow's botany classes continued so successfully and that the children exhibited such enthusiasm even at a period when it was very difficult to keep children in the area attending school at all regularly. The professor was a gifted teacher and kept the children hard at work even in the Easter term when he was in Cambridge giving his lecture course there. As for their weekly exercises at this period of the year, Henslow reports "they do not absolutely discontinue them whilst I am absent for they are regularly transmitted by post, as book parcels."[9] The School Report, 1859, tells of the popularity of the subject at Hitcham school. Only for want of desk space was Henslow forced to limit his class to forty-two volunteers. (There were eight-three children on the roll that year.)

The school herbarium was built up from plants collected by the children themselves and each week local flowers belonging to the Order concerned were exhibited in the classroom.[10] Wild flowers collected by the children were placed in a bottle-rack designed by Henslow and made by the village carpenter—a simple arrangement to be copied and exhibited at the South Kensington Museum in 1858.[11]

Organised excursions in the field were a most prestigious activity for the young botanists and were open only to those whom Henslow deemed to have enough knowledge to benefit from them. The printed schedule given to each pupil in the botany class states,

"Botanical excursions attended only by those who obtained sufficient number of marks at Monday lessons. Two picnic excursions during the summer, within the precincts of the Parish open to children in each of the three classes. Other excursions in the Parish are open only to those of the second and first classes. An excursion to a distance from the Parish to those of the first class who obtain the requisite marks."

Although these excursions must have been much less sophisticated and demanding than those led by the professor in his Cambridge context (see Chapter Two), he obviously thought them a most worthwhile educational exercise. He wrote in the *Gardeners' Chronicle*, 26th July 1856, that "occasional walks for an hour or two with children of the first class afford opportunities for awakening curiosity and imparting information".[22] He sought here, as elsewhere, to encourage students to observe and think for themselves.

The field party grew in size so that in the following July Henslow reported to Knights[13]

"I am to convey a dozen of my Village Botanists on Saturday to Great Waldingfield—A party of above thirty of them attacked Hitcham Wood this afternoon.—Botany is quite in the ascendant this afternoon."

An excursion "to a distance from the Parish" is recorded in an enquiry to Knights[14] in August, 1857. Henslow enquired,

"If I get my botanical class over to Ipswich pretty early what time could we get a boat to Harwich and back to get a few hours botanising on the marshes?"

These pupils of his first class certainly had wonderful opportunities for studying the subject widely and under expert tuition.

The prestige attached to excursions in the field was confirmed in conversation by an octogenarian Hitcham farmer, tenth of a family of twelve, whose eldest brother, William, had been one of Henslow's botanists. "The professor made the children work hard," he claimed, "and selected those to go on expeditions very carefully." William's nephew added proudly that Uncle Buffalo[15] was "a walking encyclopaedia —there wasn't a weed or grass he couldn't name".

The village botanists clearly had their eyes open in the fields of Suffolk. Their vigilance and observation led to additions to a list of the *Flora of Suffolk* compiled by Henslow and published in 1860. Additions to the Hitcham list were quaintly recorded by Henslow in his Parish Accounts! We consequently know that nine plants were added in 1852, the very first year his botany classes were held. Long-established Hitcham families read their names in the success lists. In 1858, for example, Maria Gosling, Harriet Sewell and Susan Baker succeeded in finding "larkspur and golden saxifrage", "common thorn apple and branched burr-reed" and "beaked parsley" respectively.

These youngsters figure elsewhere in the intensely human story of Hitcham's botanists and their achievements. Thus Maria Gosling received mention in next year's lists while the other two girls received prizes specially donated. Henslow's own daughter and her husband, Major

Barnard, awarded Harriet Sewell an herbarium cabinet for outstanding achievement in botany. This interesting pupil continued at the school as their first pupil-teacher and later she travelled abroad as a governess. Testimony to her continued interest in botany was found in the Sewell's Hitcham home. There her relatives proudly keep specimens of flowers collected on Miss Sewell's travels in Italy and Australia—flowers pressed and labelled according to the methods learnt by "Aunt Harriet at Hitcham Parish School." Susan Baker, the other prizewinner, received a copy of Professor Lindley's book on *School Botany* presented by the author himself.

It should be noted too that Lindley, Henslow's friend and fellow examiner at London University, was an East Anglian and his wife was from Suffolk. He visited Hitcham occasionally and was long an admirer of the excellent educational work Henslow achieved there. He assisted Henslow in the best way he could by publicising his educational work in a journal—the *Gardeners' Chronicle*—of which he was editor, and by donating prizes to the village scientists young and old. Amongst these were prizes given to botanists for their school work and, also, to the winners in the "botanical nosegay" competitions held at Hitcham's horticultural shows.

Another interesting and informed recognition of the skills of Henslow's young village botanists is found in the correspondence between Darwin and his old tutor Henslow. If is fascinating to read in these letters that Darwin sought to involve the children in the collection of seeds for his experimental work on species. In the following letter,[16] for example, he enquired about the collection of seeds to undergo immersion tests to find whether certain common species could have withstood the long seaborne journey from the Azores. It seems, in respect of identification of flowers, Darwin respected the Hitcham children's botanical knowledge more than his own!

"Down Farnborough Kent.
July 2nd 1855.

My dear Henslow,

—Now it has occurred to me that it would be an interesting way of testing the probability of sea-transportal of seeds, to make a list of all the European plants found in the Azores,—a very oceanic archipelago—collect seeds and try if they would stand a pretty long immersion.— Do you think the most able of your little girls would like to collect for me a packet of seeds of such plants as grow near Hitcham, I paying, say 3d for each packet: it would put a few shillings into their pockets and would be an ENORMOUS advantage to me, for I grudge the time to collect the seeds, more especially, as *I have to learn the plants!* The experiment seems worth trying; what do you think? Should you object to offering this reward or payment to your little girls? you would have to select the most conscientious ones, that I might not get wrong seeds . . .

My dear old Master,
Yours affectionately,
C. Darwin.

P.S. Perhaps 3d would be hardly enough; and if the number does not turn out very great it shall be 6d a packet."

Evidently Henslow agreed to the project and final instructions are sent by Darwin[17] on 14th July

"Down Farnborough Kent.
July 14th 1855.

My dear Henslow,

With mistakes & alterations, the Hitcham list is so blotched, that I have copied out the 22 plants, which grow at Hitcham & are found at Azores; & are according to a list of 77 received yesterday, from Mr. H. C. Watson, the least likely to have been imported with agricultural seeds.—If you will employ your little girls to collect these, I shd. be greatly obliged, and pay them LIBERALLY FOR ME. I shd. require, when such could be procured, a packet with 100 or 200 seeds of each kind, or even rather more of the easily procured kinds; of course less would do. But I have to try them without salting, & at successive periods after immersion.—I think I shd. prefer waiting till you have a good many (of the 22 added) kinds together. I hope that you think the experiment sufficiently curious to repay you in some slight degree for part of [the] trouble you have so kindly taken. I hope that the little girls, with payment in view, will enjoy the job.—

Most truly yours
C. Darwin.

[list of seed required]
Water-cress—nasturtium officinale
Milkwort
[*Strawberry* del] Fragaria vesca
[*Silver weed* del] Cinque-foil, creeping Potentilla reptans
Cinquefoil strawberry-leaved P. tormentilla
[*Willow* del]—herb—small-flowered. Epilob. Parviflorum.
Water-star-wort Callitriche
Ivy   Hedera   helix
Marsh-wort procumbant   Helosciadium nodiflorum
Bedstraw, white water   Galium palustre
Centaury common   Erythraea centauria
Hooded-Bindweed, great.   Convolvulus sepium
Primrose   Primula veris
Figwort water   Scrophularia aquatica

Speedwell thyme-leaved.	Veronica serpyllifolia
,, water	,, anagallis
,, common	,, officinalis
Thrincia hairy-	Thrincia hirta
Spurge-laurel, common	Daphne laureola
Club Rush, lake	Scirpus lacustris
Carex—	any 2 species

22 kinds   ''

Later that summer Darwin is challenged to investigate current pro-
nouncements by two naturalists concerning the fertility of plants. Again
he needed material for the investigation and the Hitcham botanists come
to mind. The whole letter[18] (without postscript) is included here for it
mostly deals with the issues in hand. It would be of interest to know how
much the young collectors knew of the nature of their mission. Bearing in
mind the professor's general enthusiasm, it is likely he shared some of
this excitement with his pupils by telling them of the scientist hard at work
in Downe.

Down 23rd [Aug/Sept 1855?]

My dear Henslow,

The enclosed Umbellifer has made me very unhappy: I cannot make
it out: will you name it for me? I hate the whole Family. It grew
[3-4 ft *added*] in rather moist thicket. To save trouble I send
envelope all ready directed.—On account of two statements made by
naturalists, *viz* (one) that the most 'typical form of a species is that
which produces most seed,' I am very anxious to compare number of
seed of wild & cultivated plants (I can easily see how false the above
aphorism is [but I want precise facts *added*]) & I most curiously
forget it wd. not suffice to count seeds of one umbel of Wild Celery so
will you get one of your little girls to get very finest ½ wild Celery near
you, & either count (& pay well for me) all the seeds, or count
umbels, & count seeds in an average umbel.—I can manage Carrot &
Parsnip myself, & have wild & tame plants, marked. I have got wild
Cabbage & asparagus, also, in hand.—[our wild Parsnips are poor,
so perhaps it wd. be good to let some little girl count *added*]. There
has been another more wonderful statement made than even the
above,—*viz* that rich cultivation (not merely of the individual but of
the race) *lessens* the fertility of all organic beings, by which assumption
several [authors *added*] (as I daresay you may have noticed) have
attempted to upset Malthus' most logical writing—I mention all this
just to show that my odd wishes are not *absolutely* idle. Most truly
yours

C. Darwin.

Acknowledging the practical response evoked in Hitcham, Darwin wrote[19] on 10th November.

"I am *very much* obliged for the seeds, especially for the experimental seeds. I send a postal order for 10s. for a douceur for your good little Botanists, and I am sure the girl who counted the parsnip seeds deserves a perfect dowry—. . ."

If there were any criticism of Henslow's botany teaching by his scientific friends it was focused on his insistent use of technical terms by the youngsters. Basic terms from which the beginners might deduce further information were not so much in question. In fact the deductive process which they facilitated was seen as one of the merits of the teaching exercise. Joseph Hooker, for example, told his father-in-law that he agreed to the necessity of mastering a name which "conveys definite information" such as "Ranunculaceoous" and "perigynous" "if the learner is going to progress in Botany". He took Henslow to task, however, for introducing too many difficult words in his proposed textbook for beginners. He comments in a letter[20] dated 12th December, 1854,

"My own impression is, that it would be better to make the demonstration of the Bean first, simple, clear and to the point, giving no words except the simplest. I object to 'axis', 'relative', 'modification' etc., when super-added to the necessary and unavoidable technicalities; each of these, though familiar to us, being a subject of thought to the 'village school' before understood."

Hooker's wife, Henslow's daughter Frances, had also read the manuscript and found the same objection. The letter thus continues,

"Fanny has been looking over parts of it, and quite agrees with me that the words underlined in pencil will be so many stumbling-blocks to village school children and even higher class ones. In short the whole is not only too scientific but in too scientific language."

George Bentham (co-author with Hooker of the famous *Flora of the British Isles*) also regarded the use of technical terms with beginners in botany as a matter of note and perhaps of question. In reply to Henslow's comments on his book for beginners, Bentham writes[21] in May, 1857,

". . . I wanted my book to be generally useful for those who would take it up for a pastime during occasional short visits to the country or in moments of leisure or botanical whim and I cannot expect this class (who I believe to be numerous) to be learned and technical like your schoolgirls. One of your schedules or such words as verticillaster would, I fear, make the person I allude to shut up the book and take to other amusement."

He is, however, gracious enough to admit that he would follow Henslow's lead if he were considering school botany, and adds

"If my book had been 'for use of schools' I should have made it more technical and include a number of plants of which specimens might easily be obtained for examination . . ."

*   *   *

But while men of science generally applauded Henslow's pioneer science teaching in the Hitcham school there were others who did not, and the struggle for recognition was a bitter one especially within the parish bounds themselves.

Criticism of school botany took two forms in the parish. The objections either stressed the irreligious nature of science and, by implication, opposed the teaching of it, or they stated that the time spent in teaching botany took precious time available for more important subjects, be they religious studies or other basic subjects.

Fear of science was not new to the nineteenth century but the threats to established beliefs had been renewed and intensified by geologists of the period who had called into question the time scale of the earth's formation and existence of life upon it. Lyell's *Principles of Geology*, published in 1830, had fanned the fire of the science v. religion controversy. Henslow, himself, had faith that all facts revealed by science would accord with religion and enable man the better to appreciate God's works. This was the stand made explicit in the *Bridgewater Treatises* written by eminent British scholars explaining the controversy and publishing their views, 1835-1840[22].

In his address at the opening of Ipswich Natural History Museum in 1848, Professor Henslow publicly expressed his defence of teaching science to the people.[23] He countered his religious critics in militant terms. First, he stated—

"If they tell me that science is necessarily a snare and an obstruction to our spiritual progress, I tell them, in return. that I utterly deny and disbelieve their assertions."

He then turned specifically to botany teaching and, in particular, the method of investigating the specimens scientifically and inducing laws from observed facts. He countered the criticisms here in religious terms.

"Can they suppose that a closer inspection of the lilies of the field than they have an inclination to give them will necessarily compel us to acknowledge that these good creatures of God have now lost somewhat in comparison of their clothing with that of the richest garments of an earthly potentate? . . .

Let us be mutually tolerant, mutually confiding, and then in due course, we shall learn to see how impossible it is that either the works of God or the word of God can ever be teaching us things contradictory to truth."

Further to this declaration of his faith in the unity of knowledge Henslow proceeded to comfort those who feared that the pursuit of science might sap their spiritual strength. He emphasised that in this activity as in all others there is a supreme need for faith in God's Word.

"Of this I am quite sure, that where the study of God's works is combined with a sure faith in His Word, the former can in no respect impair our spiritual possession of the life that now is, or deprive us of the enjoyment of one jot or tittle of those glorious promises which have assured us of immortality."

But while he had countered these serious and direct expressions of doubt about the pursuit of natural history in general, Henslow could not prevent the growth of unease amongst parishioners when he first introduced botany into Hitcham school. The unease manifested itself in criticism of the balance of subject teaching in the school. Although botany was entirely a voluntary subject so that no-one could justifiably complain that it took time from other subjects, complaints there were. At the turn of the century, the professor's son investigated the validity of such earlier allegations and received an unequivocal refutation by one of Her Majesty's Inspectors of National Schools.[24] With specific reference to the standard of religious teaching at Hitcham School, the Inspector informed George Henslow that

". . . The religious teaching given in Hitcham School was quite equal to any imparted to poor children in parish schools in general. The children always showed a competent acquaintance with the scriptures and with those chief truths upon which Christian life is based."

He further asserted

"I had no reason to think that the botanical lessons interfered with a due study of the usual subjects of a National School. Independently of the botany, Hitcham ranked well among the better class of rural school in the district inspected. The Professor gave a just weight to all subjects of the school, in my opinion."

Further light is thrown on the healthy balance of subjects in Henslow's school at this period by his own School Reports. Even allowing for the fact that the professor wrote them himself, there seems enough evidence to corroborate the Inspector's memory that secular subjects were given their "just weight". Thus Henslow reports, in 1854, that the accuracy of the dictation was good and the writing extremely good; recitation of poems was performed with accuracy and understanding; and answers to questions in arithmetic, geography, history and grammar were good considering the short time they had been receiving instruction in these subjects. In 1856—and this was the year in which the Science and Art Department recognised Henslow's school botany by asking him to design a series of botanical diagrams and an instructional pamphlet for schools—the Hitcham school report again expresses satisfaction with the answers to questions on geography, history and grammar at the second examination held by Her Majesty's Inspectors at the school since its remodelling as a National School. Again, in a letter to Knights[25] of Ipswich in 1858, Henslow writes of the fourth school Inspection, remarking that "all has gone off satisfactorily".

Firm evidence of the general efficiency of the school is implied by its recognition, in 1856, as a suitable establishment for educating pupil-teachers. Government grants for this purpose had been available to efficient schools since 1845 and the system was valuable to both the schools and the pupil-teachers themselves. The achievements of Hitcham's first pupil-teacher, Harriet Sewell, certainly help to substantiate that all-round and effective education had been provided by the school. In 1861, the *Report of the Committee of Council on Education* notes under the list of candidates awarded Queen's Scholarships (about eight hundred training college places were available to young women in this scheme), "Females . . . Sewell, H., Hitcham." She was twentieth in her year. Harriet Sewell did not remain in school teaching all her life and after a short while became governess to the Bryce family with whom, we have seen, she travelled widely. Reference has already been made to her continued botanical interests during those travels. But, more relevant here, is the fact that "Aunt Harriet's scrap book", still treasured at her Hitcham home, contains a captivating log of her journeys written in an effective and educated prose style conveying colourful description and thoughtful reflection. Her education, received entirely at this little village school, took her even further professionally and it is recorded in the scrapbook that the latter part of her life was spent as superintendent of a "Home for ladies whose means had dwindled". This Victorian lady, revered by her relatives to this day, was strong in character and a keen, tenacious worker. Her achievements were certainly due to her own persistence and ability but the opportunities to develop her talents and encouragement to do so were first provided by the professor and his school.

The professor's own estimate of the success of the general teaching in his school was further confirmed by an elderly lady resident of Hitcham whose own mother had attended the school during Henslow's time. She referred to her mother as "a well-educated woman" who wrote very well "in a lovely hand" until the very end of her life. A sample of her work showed that her figures were beautifully executed also and she obviously had made good progress in her arithmetic. The husband admired his wife's great learning and had frequently impressed upon his children (of whom the informant was one) that "there was not a word in the dictionary that your mother could not spell". Perhaps it is even more important to note that this woman had been very happy at the school.

One aspect of this lady's work, needlework, deserves special mention.

The old lady had in her possession some exquisite samplers worked by her mother while at school. The care and precision of the work is remarkable and it is hard to understand why parents complained that insufficient time was given to needlework at the school. Yet this was one of the specific and recurring complaints received by the rector. Certainly some timetabled time had been taken from the subject when arithmetic, geography, history and grammar had been introduced in 1854 to comply with curriculum requirements for National Schools. No needlework time had been transferred to botany when this subject had been introduced two years before! Henslow faced these unreasonable complaints squarely and enjoined an angered parent, "Do not expect your daughter to do the household needlework during school hours".

The charge that normal school subjects suffered because of the introduction of voluntary botany classes was a continuing one but is refuted by the accumulated evidence of pupil achievement and contemporary report. Even in 1859, when the schoolmistress retired through ill-health, the inspectors had no criticism of the learning standards in the school. Henslow writes in his Annual Report that on the morning of the annual examination that year one of the examiners had expressed himself satisfied, with one exception, viz; that he did not consider the children so orderly and thoroughly disciplined as he could have wished.

Even though this Inspector's report did not directly criticise the general teaching of the school, Henslow took the adverse comments very seriously. In response to the challenge he personally accompanied his daughter, the schoolmistress, two pupil-teachers and two or three girls from the first class on a visit arranged by the Inspector to a London girls' school, the London Orphan Asylum at Clapton. Here, the Inspector explained with circumlocution in a letter to Jenyns, that the party were to see "carried out into practice, and in a high degree of perfection, methods of discipline enforced by moral power and accompanied by such standards of attainment in children as would fall within the compass of their own judgements to form an estimate of meeting in a practical manner, suggestion of improvement in his [Henslow's] school-teaching power, which had been elicited and canvassed between us at my recent visit of Inspection at Hitcham."[26]

That there was room for improvement at Hitcham school at that time cannot be denied. The illness of the schoolmistress eventually caused academic standards to fall and the Reverend Meyrick, in the 1860 Report on the school, stated that the children "did not pass a good examination in arithmetic, and their spelling needs great attention on the part of the mistress".[27] What is categorically refuted both by the Inspector's comments and by the request for Henslow to give a botany lecture at the Clapton school is any suggestion that botany teaching was undermining or taking time from essential studies. The professor evidently gave a successful botany lecture to the Orphans' school and won the admiration of the Inspector whose report to Jenyns admits

"The result was a most interesting lecture, which brought quite within the limits of their childish comprehension a subject entitled, 'Vegetables the ultimate source of Food to Man'. He was too, at pains to bring with him a large box of specimens with which to illustrate his lecture . . ."

Whatever local doubts remained, Henslow's botany teaching had clearly received official recognition by the Committee of Council on Education through Her Majesty's Inspectors. Early in 1859, in response to an official request, the professor wrote to Reverend M. Mitchell, Inspector of Schools, outlining the botany teaching at Hitcham. It was published by the Committee of Council and other teachers could introduce Henslow's controversial teaching methods into their schools in the expectation of receiving official blessing. Indeed, the Reverend M. Mitchell prefaced Henslow's letter with an explicit, if muted, benediction:[28]

"My attention has been directed to the teaching of botany at the country village school at Hitcham, Suffolk. The subjoined letter from the Rev. J. S. Henslow, The Professor of Botany at Cambridge fully explains his system and I can imagine that the study usefully directs the attention of his pupils to observe the beauties of nature amongst which they dwell."

"Hitcham, Bildeston, Suffolk.
7 January, 1859.

My Dear Sir,

The botanical lessons which I give at our village school every Monday afternoon is divided into an 'educational exercise' and an 'instructional lecture'. The exercise is worked by the children as methodically as they would go through a sum in arithmetic, and it forms an important feature of these lessons that they are not allowed to shirk the few hard words in which the more essentially important scientific ideas are embodied. This part of the exercise serves also to increase their powers of correct spelling, as I require the strictest orthography in the 2 or 3 words required every week for designating the orders which are to be reviewed at the lecture. The Monday exercise (including the 'hard words') is all that is compulsory with the volunteers who form my botanical class. But voluntary exercises are also encouraged during the week for the purpose of procuring familiarity with the names of our native plants and their position in the natural system.

The instructional lecture, after the exercise, is not confined to botanical details. It is designed to convey a variety of information, capable of being associated (however remote the affinity) with the account of a few dried specimens selected from the school herbarium. As this selection is made continuously, the whole of the herbarium passes under review within a twelve month. It is in fact divided into thirty six lectures. The lecture-room (our class-room) is fitted for the suspension of one or two of my diagrams (prepared for the Kensington Museum), the display of the dried herbarium specimens and a map of the world. I find the American-cloth pins far more useful than the plan I have explained and illustrated in the Kensington Museum. I proceed as follows: —

1. Geography—the localities of places which will be alluded to during the lecture are just mentioned and called for. Any that are not known to the children are then pointed out; this avoids interruptions as the lecture proceeds.
2. Structure—the names of the dried specimens exhibited are then called for, and referred to their position on the printed plant lists in the hands of the children. Any striking peculiarities in the structure of a particular species, genera or orders are noticed but minute details are passed over, as the children have not the means of examining the specimens for themselves. If an order happens to be represented on a diagram, additional particulars therein illustrated are explained. Mere cram-work is avoided as much as possible though in this, as in other sciences, a certain amount of detail must be committed to memory.
3. Physiology—Any physiological fact which happens to admit of being well illustrated by an order under review is then noticed, including the geographical distribution of particular species.
4. Historical Notices—Plants alluded to in Scripture or especially referred to in History, or by authorities of note, often afford opportunities for digression.
5. Economics—Many orders admit of specimens being exhibited which are used as medicine, food, dyes and other purposes. Instructive digressions can hereby be introduced at the discretion of the lecturer. We always wind up by tasting something or other which has been followed by a product (or perhaps is a product itself) belonging either to an order under review, or to some other more or less closely allied to it!

Believe me, etc.
(Signed)   J. S. HENSLOW."

Although the battle had begun as science v. religion, it had perhaps been won more by educational arguments than theological ones. Certainly, Henslow placed increasing emphasis on the educational benefits of the study as the campaign advanced. In 1855, he borrowed arguments from the current faculty psychology[29] added a theological gloss and then asserted from the pulpit,[30]

". . . I would never consent to abandon any form of teaching which is adapted to educate and improve those mental faculties which God has bestowed upon children expressly that they may be rendered useful to their progress in after life."

Later proclamations made in articles in Professor Lindley's *Gardener's Chronicle*, 5th July 1856,[31] also reveal an accumulating list of "faculties" which botany can educate. Referring to students of botany at Hitcham school Henslow claimed—

"Observant faculties have been strengthened,
reasoning powers expanded,
the intellectual and moral status improved."

Later in this series of articles he maintained the claim of botany as an essential part of a liberal education.[32] This view he shared with no less a scholar than the eminent philosopher of science William Whewell, Master of Trinity College, Cambridge who similarly saw botany as a desirable part of liberal education.[33] Henslow's justification for this view was based on the scientific thinking essential to systematic botany. The investigatory exercises were at once the contentious elements in Henslow's teaching and his most important contributions to it. He thus raised botany from a kind of "busy idleness" or "harmless occupation"[34] to a scientific study in its own right. He never abandoned this essentially scientific nature of his teaching.

Other educational justifications for teaching botany were added to the growing list of its virtues. A school report of 1857 attributes to the study of botany—"habits of patience, perseverance and caution". Further, in 1859, Henslow recorded in his school report that when his pupils study botany it induces them to carry on sundry volunteer exercises in writing and spelling. Darwin had earlier realised the potential of school botany in the learning and use of language. A letter to Henslow, 11th December, 1853,[35] pointed out the superiority this approach would have over the conventional classical teaching.

"Now that my children are growing up and I think of educational processes, I often reflect over your inimitable (as it appears to me) good plan of teaching correct, concise languages and accurate observation, namely by making your pupils describe leaves etc. I never profited myself by this, but often wish I had. Has it ever occurred to you, (I have often wished for something of the kind) that a most useful volume might be published, with woodcut outlines, and Saxon, and not scientific English? What a habit it would give youths of thinking of the meaning of words, and what powers of expressing themselves! Compare such habits with wretched Latin verses . . ."

By extolling its educational virtues, Henslow and his friends brought the teaching of botany to the notice of educationists of the day. By his own example he showed them how it could be achieved with enjoyment and success. It now remained for other teachers in the nation's schools to follow his example.

VILLAGE SCH

Children wishing to learn Botany will be placed in the Third Class, when they shall have learnt to spell correctly the following words:—

CLASS.	DIVISION.	SECTION.
(I. *Exercise.*)	(II. *Exercise*.)	(IV. *Exercise*.)
1. Dicotyledons.	⎧ 1. Angiospermous. ⎨ ⎩ 2. Gymnospermous.	⎧ 1. Thalamifloral. ⎪ 2. Calycifloral. ⎨ 3. Corollifloral. ⎪ (V. *Exercise.*) ⎩ 4. Incomplete.
	(III. *Exercise.*)	
2. Monocotyledons.	⎧ 1. Petaloid. ⎨ ⎩ 2. Glumaceous.	⎰ 1. Superior. ⎱ 2. Inferior.
3. Acotyledons.		

Children in the Third Class, who have learnt how to fill in the first column of the Floral Schedule, and to spell correctly the following words, will be raised to the Second Class:—

Pistils and ⎫
Carpels ⎬ of Ovary (with Ovules), Style, and Stigma.
Stamens, of Filament and Anther (with Pollen).
Corolla, of Petals ⎫ or Perianth, of Leaves.
Calyx, of Sepals ⎭

Children of the Second Class who have learnt how to fill in the second column of the Floral Schedule, and to spell correctly the following words, will be raised to the First Class:—

C. Mono-di-, &c., to poly-phyllous, -sepalous, -petalous, -gynous, V. Mon-di-, &c., to poly-androus, -adelphous. Di-, tetra-. dynamous. Syngenesious.	V. C.	V. C.	V. C.
	0. An- A-	5. Pent-⎫	10. Dec-⎫
	1. Mon- o-	6. Hex- ⎪	11. Endee-⎬ a
	2. Di- —	7. Hept- ⎬ a-	12. Dodee-⎪
	3. Tri- —	8. Oct- ⎪	20. Icos- ⎭
	4. Tetr- a-	9. Enne- ⎭	00. Poly-

Children of the First Class will learn to fill in the third column of the Floral Schedule, and to spell correctly the following words:—

Hypogynous.   Perigynous.   Epigynous.
Epipetalous.   Gynandrous.

Monday Botanical Lessons at 3 p.m., at the School, to include,

1st.— Inspection of a few species, consecutively, in the order on the plant-list. Anything of interest in their structure or properties will then be noticed.

2nd.— Hard word exercises. Two or three words named one Monday are to be correctly spelt the next Monday.

3rd.— Specimens examined, and the parts of the flower laid in regular order upon the dissecting-boards. The Floral Schedule to be traced upon the slates, and filled up as far as possible. Marks to be allowed according to the following scale:—

	NO.	COHESION, PROPORTION.	ADHESION (INSERTION).	CLASSIFICA-TION.
P.	1	a-, mono-, &c., gynous 2	Superior or Inferior 2	
C.	3			Class 1
St.	1	an-, mon-, &c., androus 2	Hypo-, &c., gynous 4	Division 2
f.-	1	mon-, &c., adelphous 3 Di-, tetra-, dynamous 3	Epipetalous 4	Section 3 Order 4
a.-	1	Syngenesious 2	Gynandrous 3	Genus 3
C. P.	1	a-, mono-, &c., petalous 2	Hypo-, &c., gynous 4	Species 2
C. S.	1	a-, mono-, &c., sepalous 2	Inferior or Supe-	
or P. L.	1	a-, mono-, &c., phyllous 2	rior 2	

4th.— Questions respecting Root ; Stems and Buds ; Leaf and Stipules ; Inflorescence and Bracts ; Flower and Ovules ; Fruit ; Seed and Embryo.

Regulations respecting Botanical Prizes and Excursions.

Prizes awarded according to the joint number of marks obtained at Monday Lessons, from Schedule Labels filled in at home, and for species first found in flower during the season.

Botanical Excursions attended only by those who obtain a sufficient number of marks at Monday Lessons. Two Picnic Excursions during the summer, within the precincts of the parish, open to children in each of the three Classes. Other Excursions within the parish are open only to those of the Second and First Classes. An Excursion to a distance from the parish for those of the First Class only who obtain the requisite marks.

The First Class may attend (at the proper season) at the Rectory on Sundays, after Divine Service in the afternoon. Objects of Natural History, in the Animal, Vegetable, and Mineral Kingdoms, will then be exhibited, and such accounts given of them as may tend to improve our means of better appreciating the wisdom, power, and goodness of the Creator.

A copy of the above scheme is given to every child, however young, who is ambitious of being classed as a volunteer Botanist.

Example of a Floral Schedule filled up.

			Cl. Dicotyledons.
P.	1	Monogynous. Superior.	Div. Angiospermous.
C.	2		
St.	6	Tetradynamous. Hypogynous. Hexandrous.	Sec. Thalamifloral.
C. P.	4	Tetrapetalous. Hypogynous.	Ord. Brassicanths.
C. S.	4	Tetrasepalous. Inferior.	Gen. Wallflower.
HARRIET SEWELL, NO. 7.			Sp. Common.

CHAPTER FIVE

Botany Teaching and the Nation

THE description below relates to summer 1952—one hundred years after Professor Henslow had first introduced botany as a scientific study to his village pupils at Hitcham. The author was aware of a group of school-girls in neat blue summer dresses clustered round a modest display of wild flowers on a shelf outside the junior classroom. The flowers, supported in a simple wooden bottle rack, had been culled from the school's botanic garden and labelled carefully before the school teaching day began. The pupils were attracted to the exhibit and later they mounted the stairs to a brightly-lit biology laboratory where they found laid out for each of them a flower, a handlens, mounting needles and a scalpel. Each girl observed her flower carefully, removed some of the parts, counted the parts and entered her findings in a simple schedule suggested by the experienced biology teacher. For some years this teacher had guided youngsters through such observational exercises and had discussed with her charges the beauty of the floral specimens and their simple grouping or classification.

The scene is almost interposable with a Hitcham village botany class held a hundred years before. The botany teacher's aim and methods had changed little, the absorption of the pupils in their task was as great. Four differences were, however, discernible and significant. Firstly, the "wild" flowers were specially grown in the school botanic garden of this urban school and not brought in by the children from the fields. Secondly, the work room was a specially designed biology laboratory which at other times facilitated experimental work now included in the botanical studies. Further, the schedule used by these twentieth century girl botanists demanded far fewer "hard words" than Henslow would have required of his village children.[1] And, finally, the social background of the young ladies contrasted greatly with Henslow's Hitcham school children of the "labouring classes". The class described above were daughters of business executives, artists and teachers attending a fee-paying public school in the London suburbs in the nineteen-fifties.

The pattern for botany teaching in English schools had been set for a century and more by Professor Henslow at his Hitcham school. Henslow's work had influenced botany classes in elementary schools, in public and grammar schools and colleges and, to some extent, in the private and proprietary schools of the late nineteenth century and beyond. The professor had taught school botany at Hitcham for ten years, 1851-1861, and although he lived only a short while after the public recognition of this successful enterprise, fellow botanists—many Henslow's friends and relations—carried the spirit of his work forward into the twentieth century.

In the last few years of his life, Henslow's school botany teaching attracted considerable national attention which culminated, as we have seen, in the publication of a summary of his teaching scheme by the Committee of Council on Education in 1859. Earlier and purely factual recognition of his work appeared in the Committee's Annual Report of 1856. Its author merely noted,

"Botany is taught, and well, in Professor Henslow's school, as Mr Campbell informs me."

—not, one might think, an over-enthusiastic commendation. Nevertheless, Lyon Playfair at the newly formed Department of Science and Art at South Kensington was more discerning and sought copies of Henslow's teaching materials for public exhibition there. Early in 1856, Playfair commissioned a series of diagrams such as had been used in the Hitcham school to illustrate the various Orders of plants under investigation. The professor had engaged the help of his daughter, Mrs Barnard, in preparing the original illustrations. The final drawings were executed by Walter Fitch,[2] formerly a pattern drawer in a calico factory, and later official draughtsman for official Kew publications. He had the sheets ready by mid-April. A contract was then negotiated[3] which included an agreement to pay Fitch ten guineas for his work. Playfair kept Henslow informed of progress—

"Marlborough House
(no date)

My dear Sir,

I am glad you have got Fitch's Diagrams complete. The best plan probably would be to send it here, when we would get Day's estimate and then estimate of their contractors as to the execution of the series.

I forget whether the number you contemplated was 10 or 12 . . .

Yours truly,
Lyon Playfair."

"Marlborough House
19th April 1856.

My dear Sir,

Messrs. Day have won the contract for your Diagrams, and I have prepared a minute on the subject which will pass, I trust, on Saturday.

The price will be 4/8d for Schools, buying directly from Day, and about 2/4d buying directly from the Department including your Royalty.

The next contract was 7/- for schools, so I have little doubt Mess.r.s. Day have made it as small as they could.

Yours sincerely,
Lyon Playfair,

P.S. The estimate went upon the suggestion that 10 guineas or pounds was to be paid to Fitch."

A year later the diagrams had reached proof stage and the Department were now seeking a "typical herbarium" for exhibition. Knights, his friend and museum curator at Ipswich, was kept abreast of these moves.[4] On 24th April, 1857 Henslow referred to the "village machinery" who were to be engaged in preparing this exhibit for the nation when he returned from Cambridge on completion of his teaching term.

". . . The Department of Science and Art have engaged me to superintend the preparation of a typical herbarium for Schools—as soon as I get back, I shall set my Village Machinery at work for the purpose.

[P.S] I have now seen proofs of the Diagrams."

By midsummer the botanical diagrams were on exhibition. Playfair was obviously satisfied and wrote to Henslow[5] from the Department of Science and Art, 15th July 1857,

". . . Your diagrams have got an excellent place in the Museum and are very much admired."

The exhibition of educational materials at South Kensington—the pre-runner of the current Science Museum—was part of a move by the Science and Art Department to further science education in the nation's schools. Geological, mineralogical and other exhibits were displayed and an opening course was given to masters in training colleges and elementary schools to explain the collection. The second course of lectures was given by Henslow's friend Professor Lindley who spoke to teachers and students of Art "On the Art of teaching Systematical Botany".[6] In spite of the title it seems likely that Lindley made clear the scientific value of teaching the subject. He and Henslow had worked in harmony in the field for many years and had together established practical examinations in botany in the Universities of London and Cambridge.

In spite of Playfair's initiative and drive, science made a slow entry into the elementary schools. Just at a time when the science campaign seemed to be gathering momentum, all attempts to broaden the curriculum were arrested by the introduction of the "payment by results" scheme to the state's schools. In 1862, Robert Lowe as Secretary of State to the Committee of Council brought in his restricting Revised Code and subjects such as botany were sacrificed to an attempted improvement of the 3 Rs. Teachers were paid according to the success of their pupils in the basic subjects and it was not unnatural than many concentrated on these to the exclusion of all else. Only with the amelioration of this crippling Code were natural history sciences encouraged again in 1871 by the award of a small grant. The botany syllabus included some elementary anatomy and plant function but mainly it was a syllabus of the Hitcham pattern. Scientific observation of fresh floral specimens received official encouragement.[7] Thus, one of Her Majesty's Inspectors in the Shrewsbury area writing of science subjects in 1879 remarked

> "I am disposed to think that botany is the most useful. If taught through personal investigation and experiment it develops power of thought and teaches the children the pleasures and habits of observations."

In spite of official backing, progress of the subject in the elementary schools remained disappointing. Only 928 children were examined in botany in 1878 and the number presented in botany was but 24,000 by 1890.[8]

* * *

Prince Albert's interest in furthering the nation's progress in the field of science and technology is well-documented. He fully realised the importance of school science to the success of this movement and his decision to arrange science lessons for the Royal children in 1858 was a triumph for the science educators and an example to the nation's schools. Professor Henslow was selected to give the botany lessons.

It is interesting to speculate how the invitation came about. Was it through Lyon Playfair at the Department of Science and Art, or through Henslow's dear friend and colleague Sir Adam Sedgwick, perhaps? He, Sedgwick, was Cambridge Secretary to the Prince and had worked closely with him since his appointment as Chancellor of the University in 1847. Or was it Sir William Hooker's recommendation or, more likely, Joseph Hooker's? Henslow had helped Sir William with the design of the museum and herbarium at Kew and was still in regular communication with him and with Joseph, now Henslow's son-in-law. The correspondence about the Royal lessons certainly referred to Dr Hooker and is presently housed at Kew.[9] Initial soundings had been made through Joseph Hooker. The Palace secretary, I. A. Clark, clearly aware that Henslow was busy in Cambridge until June and was thereafter engaged in teaching at Hitcham village school on Monday afternoons, sent this approach letter on 25th April, 1860—

> "I am very glad to hear from Dr. Hooker that you are quite willing to give the Royal Children a few lectures on Botany. Your present course of lectures terminates I understand in May, and that you will be free in June which will be a good month to give lectures. If you will let me

know what time in June will suit you and the course best, I will arrange it with the Prince Consort. Three or four lectures I presume will be sufficient, each lecture an hour, and twice a week sufficiently often—the days most convenient to you will be chosen, and we will, of course exclude Monday from the number. Owen takes Monday and Thursday but any other days will do quite as well with us, and can be made to suit your convenience. The forenoon is the time of Owen's lectures, but that too may be arranged I doubt not, to suit you. Owen gave his first lecture on the Mammalia last Monday and tomorrow gives his second on birds. There is a convenient room for exhibiting the illustrations, and you will have an attentive and pleased audience to listen to you . . ."

The duration of the teaching sessions was clearly fixed even if their placement in the week was not. The allotted hour was less time than Henslow utilised for his village botany lessons and was doubtless determined on the assumption that the teaching method was to be a straightforward lecture! True, provision was made for illustrative material to be displayed and this was ideal for the excellent diagrams Henslow used, but the letter nowhere anticipated the observation of live specimens which were the basis of Henslow's teaching at all stages. It is not surprising therefore that the second letter from Clark[10] replies sympathetically to a request to bring specimens to the Palace.

"You may come and bring your specimens to the Palace any time you please—the room in which the lectures will be given is large, and Owen had one end of it covered with green baize to which he pinned his diagrams—there are also tables in which specimens may be placed; anything you want may be got at the Palace—the room I think must to forty feet long and I should think twenty five broad and reasonably high. It is also well-lighted—any assistance or appliances you require we can get for you . . .

The days you named answer very well. The Prince went over his memoranda book and noted them—I told him that although you had passed these days you would change them if necessary—But they will do very well, and half past eleven I hope may not be too early for you, as it suits the arrangements in the [?] and attendance of Master Owen's lectures I think I told you have gone off well and gave just satisfaction, and I have no doubt yours will do the same."

With the total time limited to four hours for four lectures it was not possible for Henslow to do more than outline the nature of the study of botany and point the way to further investigation if any of the family should wish to pursue it on their own. Thus the class were not required to fill in floral schedules as Henslow's village children would have done but this did not mean that the schedule method was ignored. Far from it. Lecture one, as described by Henslow in the pages of the July *Gardeners'*

(x) Hitcham House, the old rectory.   *Richard Burn*

(xi) Hitcham Church.   *Richard Burn*

(xii) Hitcham charities—from a plaque on the wall under the bell tower of Hitcham Parish Church.

Richard Burn

(xiii) School nomination ticket.

Ipswich Record Office

VILLAGE-SCHOOL BOTANY.

Children wishing to learn Botany will be placed in the 3rd Class when they shall have learnt to spell correctly the following words.

Class.	Division.	Section.

(I. Exercise.)	*(II. Ex.)*	*(IV. Ex.)*

1. Dicotyledons	1. Angiospermous	1. Thalamifloral
		2. Calycifloral
		3. Corollifloral
		(V. Ex.)
	2. Gymnospermous	4. Incomplete
	(III. Ex.)	
2. Monocotyledons	1. Petaloid	1. Superior
		2. Inferior
	2. Glumaceous	
3. Acotyledons.		

Children in the 3rd Class who have learnt how to fill in the first column of the Floral Schedule, and to spell correctly the following words, will be raised to the Second Class.

Pistils & Carpels } of Ovary (with Ovules), Style, and Stigma.

Stamens, of Filament and Anther (with Pollen).

Corolla, of Petals } or Perianth, of Leaves.
Calyx, of Sepals

Children of the 2nd Class who have learnt how to fill in the second column of the Floral Schedule, and to spell correctly the following words will be raised to the 1st Class.

C. Mono—di—&c. to poly—phyllous,—sepalous,—petalous,—gynous.
V. Mon—di—&c. to poly—androus,—adelphous.
Di—, tetra—dynamous..................Syngenesious.

V.	C.	V.	C.	V.	C.
0. An—	A—	5. Pent—}		10. Dec—}	
1. Mon—	o—	6. Hex—}		11. Endec—}	
2. Di—	—	7. Hept—}a—	12. Dodec—}a—	
3. Tri—	—	8. Oct—}		20. Icos—}	
4. Tetr—	a—	9. Enne—}		∞. Poly—}	

Children of the 1st Class will learn to fill in the 3rd column of the Floral Schedule and to spell correctly the following words.

Hypogynous	Epipetalous
Perigynous	Gynandrous.
Epigynous	

Monday Botanical Lessons at 3 P. M. at the School, to include—

1st. Inspection of a few species, consecutively, in the order on the plant-list. Any thing of interest in their structure or properties will then be noticed.

2nd. Hard word exercises. Two or three words named one Monday are to be correctly spelt the next Monday.

3rd. Specimens examined, and the parts of the flower laid in regular order upon the dissecting boards. The Floral Schedule to be traced upon the slates, and filled up as far as possible. Marks to be allowed according to the following scale.

	No.	Cohesion, Proportion.		Adhesion (Insertion)		Classification.	
$\frac{P}{C}$	$\frac{1}{3}$	a,—mono—,&c. gynous	2	Superior or Inferior	2	Class	1
						Division	2
St.	1	a,—mon—,&c. androus	2	Hypo—&c. gynous	4	Section	3
f.—	1	{mon—,&c. adelphous	3	Epipetalous	4	Order	4
		Di,—tetra—dynamous	3			Genus	3
a.—	1	Syngenesious	2	Gynandrous	3	Species	2
{ C. P.	1	a—,mono—,&c. petalous	2	Hypo—&c. gynous	4		
{ C. S.	1	a—,mono—,&c. sepalous	2	} Inferior or			
or P. L.	1	a—,mono—,&c. phyllous	2	} Superior	2		

4th. Questions respecting Root; Stems and Buds; Leaf and Stipules; Inflorescence and Bracts; Flower and Ovules; Fruit; Seed and Embryo.

Regulations respecting Botanical Prizes and Excursions.

Prizes awarded according to the joint number of marks obtained at Monday Lessons, from Schedule Labels filled in at home, and for species first found in flower during the season.

Botanical Excursions attended only by those who obtain a sufficient number of marks at Monday Lessons. Two private Excursions during the summer, within the precincts of the Parish, open to Children in each of the three classes. Other Excursions within the parish are open only to those of the second and first classes. An Excursion to a distance from the Parish for those of the first class only who obtain the requisite marks.

The first class may attend (at the proper season) at the Rectory on Sundays after Divine Service in the advancement of Natural History, in the Animal, Vegetable, and Mineral ... as may tend to improve our means of better appreciating ...

(as taken from the original)

Ipswich Record Office

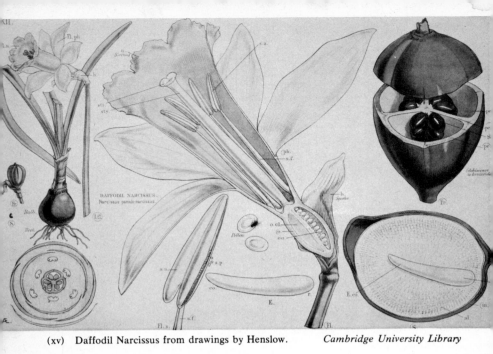

(xv) Daffodil Narcissus from drawings by Henslow. *Cambridge University Library*

(xvi) Common mallow from drawings by Henslow. *Cambridge University Library*

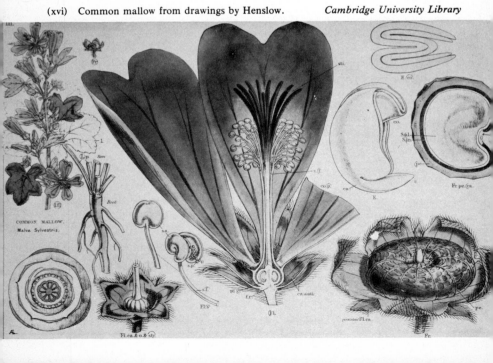

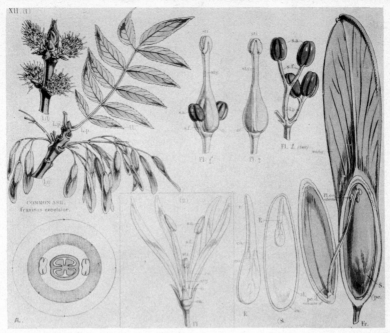

(xvii) Common ash from drawings by Henslow. *Cambridge University Library*

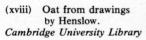

(xviii) Oat from drawings
by Henslow.
Cambridge University Library

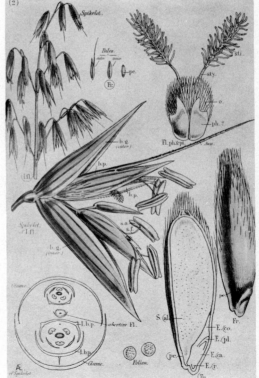

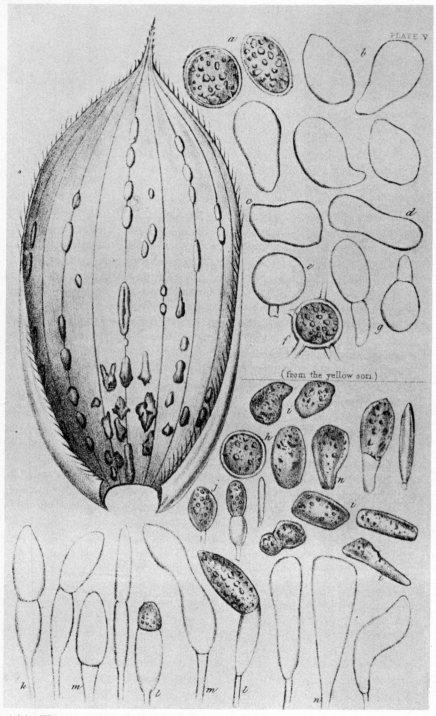

(from the yellow sori)

(xix) Wheat rust and mildew—detail discovered and drawn by Henslow.

University of Nottingham

(xx) Ploughing certificate.

HORTICULTURAL SHOW.

PROGRAMME FOR SEP. 14th, 1859.

8 to 10. A. M. Specimens for competition received at the Rectory.

12. Marquee Museum ready for inspection.

N. B. Lecturets as opportunities may occur. Among novelties observe

Animal. Skulls of Albatross, Condor, Toucan; Whales'-Food. Vertical Wasp-comb from Mexico.

Vegetable. Grater and Sieve for Manihot, with Cassava, from Brazil. Palmite Brushes from S. Africa. Chinese Sugar-grass grown at Hitcham. Skeleton leaves from China.

Mineral. Iron Pyrites (from Essex, by H. Fisher,) changing to Green Vitriol. Lava from Monah Rowah, Owyhee.

Miscellaneous. Jamaica Rat-trap. A Glass pebble found at Ringshall.

Stereoscopic Photographs on a stand near the Museum.

1. P. M. Show-booth ready for inspection.

2½. Prizes to Village Botanists for

(1) Wild-fruit Posies. The species not to exceed 20, and to be named and classed.

(2) Dried Grass Posies. The species to be named and classed.

(3) Herbarium Specimens prepared since last year. Any one who has been in the First Class, whether resident or not in Hitcham, may compete for this prize.

School Report.

3. Allotment Report; and prizes awarded for

(1) Superior Allotment Culture.

(2) Hatcher Sweepstakes.

(3) Specimens exhibited at this Day's Show.

(4) The Cottage Barometer, (by Dr. Lindley,) and a Metal Teapot, (by G. Knights, Esq.,) to the two Members of the Society who shall have obtained the greatest and next greatest number of marks for all prizes during the year.

Thanks to the Judges, Donors of Prizes, and to all others aiding and abetting our proceedings.

4. No specimens to be removed from the Show-booth before 4 P. M. Short memories are then to remind their owners to return all Check and Prize Tickets to one of the Stewards. Short days necessitate sharp movements, or we shall not have time by

5. To take our tea orderly and sociably. Rules for " ticketless babies " (0 to 2 years) and for " ticketed ditto " (2 to 4 years) continue as heretofore.

6. God save the Queen. Good night. May every one present at the Show rise to-morrow with a conscience void of offence towards God and Man, in respect of any thing said or done during a day devoted to innocent and rational recreation.

Chronicle, concerned itself with Structural Botany[11] and in the course of this lecture the Royal children were introduced to the names of various plant organs with examples. Specimens of flowering plants were examined from the seedling stage to the flowering stage and the flowers classified. It was at this stage that Henslow described the schedule that he had used for botanical exercises with his village pupils, presumably in the hope that someone might be moved to study some flower types on their own. Similarly the selection and the preparation of herbarium specimens was described with illustrative material.

In the second lecture which concerned itself with Systematic Botany,[12] Henslow introduced the class to the Linnean system of classification[13] for which he was obliged to tell of the significance of the generic and specific names of a plant. Thus the meanings of Genus, Order and Species were elucidated and nine examples were illustrated by the set of diagrams previously prepared for the Department of Science and Art, and recently placed in the South Kensington Museum as a guide to all teaching the subject.

Lecture three was devoted to Physiological Botany.[14] For the most part this consisted of relating form and function of the plants' anatomical features. There was little mention of the more recent European work in physiology (transpiration of photosynthesis) in spite of the fact that nutrition was itself referred to. Henslow confined his comments here to the chemical composition of plants. This information, recently elaborated by Liebig in Germany, had a profound importance in its application to agriculture and greatly interested Henslow.

The professor was perhaps particularly at home in lecture four which he entitled Economic Botany. The utilitarian nature of this aspect of botanical study had always appealed to him and recurs not only in his village school teaching but in lectures given to Cambridge students and to adults in the Suffolk area. There is every reason to believe that it proved interesting to the Royal audience too for he included references to poisonous and wholesome plants, a topic about which he had acquired a great store of knowledge and illustrative material.

Doubtless, the Royal lessons brought further publicity to the professor's methods of teaching botany even though he himself was far from satisfied with the classes he gave at the Palace. There was no time for proper scientific investigation and no time for field excursions, so important in his normal teaching programme.

*   *   *

Enquiries about teaching school botany were already coming in to Henslow by 1857. Locally, a Dr Drummond, known to Knights of Ipswich Museum, was clearly embarking on such teaching. A letter to Knights from Henslow,[15] dated 5th June of that year includes mention of herbarium materials which Henslow and his "village machinery" seem to have been preparing for Drummond.

". . . Tell Dr. Drummond we had a [foray?] one Wednesday in Hitcham Wood and the children found 55 specimens of Birds Nest Orchis for which I gave them ½d a piece! They are working hard at drying the specimens and I have distributed all the old newspapers he sent to me."

The following year Henslow sent Drummond and two other of Knights' acquaintances copies of his sixpenny pamphlet *Illustrations to be employed in Practical Lessons on Botany, adapted to Beginners*, published by Chapman and Hall. The type of schools for which they were destined is not clear. He simply told Knights[16]

". . . I have sent copies of the *Illustrations* to Dr. Drummond, Dr. Webster, R. Ransome—Is there anyone else in Ipswich likely to take up the subject for a school?"

Public schools would have learned more of Henslow's teaching methods when he addressed the British Association meeting in summer of 1859 on the teaching of botany to beginners.[17] A number of schoolmasters from these schools attended the meetings or read the Association's *Reports*. A master from Marlborough College, for example, applied to Henslow for advice on introducing botany at the school about that time. The subject evidently began well. Leonard Jenyns recalled,[18]

"At Marlborough College especially, I am informed the introduction of botany had been attended with great success. Botanical prizes were instituted here in May, 1860 by one of the Masters, who applied to Professor Henslow for advice on the subject, and acted principally upon his suggestions. About eight scholars went in for the prizes, and the collection of plants made by the successful candidates were very creditable."

There is no doubt that this particular science offered itself as a very acceptable inclusion in the Public Schools' ailing and out-dated curriculum. The need for liberalising the erstwhile classical education of these schools was already a matter of public debate.

A Royal Commission was set up in 1862 under the chairmanship of Lord Clarendon to look into the nine great schools and their curricula. Two important witnesses replying to questions on the curriculum of these schools spoke of the marked advantages of botany as a science of observation, ideal for school study. One of the witnesses was Dr Joseph Hooker, botanist and Henslow's son-in-law, the other was Robert Owen, the zoologist who had preceded Henslow in the series of science lectures given to the Royal children. Hooker drew specific attention to Henslow's own successful teaching[19] adding a comment which would have greatly pleased the late professor—

"the advantage of Botany is that you can teach it anywhere and everywhere. The child as he walks along can make use of his own botanical knowledge and can preserve his specimens, and, having put his information into writing, can preserve this alongside the specimen itself."

These views were incorporated in the final report published in 1864—a report which strongly recommended the liberalising of the curriculum.

The very year in which the report was published saw the introduction of botany to Rugby School, one of the nine investigated by Lord Clarendon's Commission. The school already had a thriving natural history tradition as testified by Martin in Butler's *Tom Brown's Schooldays*. Nevertheless, a scientific approach to the subject was now envisaged and Joseph Hooker and George Henslow, the late professor's botanist son, were called upon to guide the way. Wilson the mathematician who was to teach botany at Rugby, explained,[20]

> "In the summer vacation we engaged Professor George Henslow (son of the Reverend J. Henslow of Hitcham fame, and follower of his father's methods) to come with us and a party of enthusiastic lady collectors and diagram-makers, to Barmouth for six weeks' study. With that preparation, and it was not inadequate, we started with something over 35 boys in Botany in September 1864."

So, with a syllabus set out by Hooker, Henslow's diagrams and the schedule method of study,[21] the botany lessons began.

The truth was that the subject crept in as a stop-gap measure while the school waited for the Reverend T. Hutchinson to come and teach physics and chemistry. It was, however, a real success. Wilson, and Kitchener who assisted him, became most enthusiastic. Wilson addressed the British Association on the matter in 1867. In his account, "On Teaching Natural Science in Schools", 1868,[22] he claimed an increase in mental activity and logical power amongst his boys. How far this was due to the subject, the enthusiasm of the teachers or the welcome change from classical verse is an open question. One fact is established—the botanists formed a group with high morale in the school and marked their proud social solidarity by taking on the rest of the school in a two day football match. Wilson himself played for the botanists. Result unknown!

An extract from a Rugby botany lesson,[23] illustrating the investigatory method, is given by Wilson in his 1868 account and is included here.

> "Suppose then your class of thirty or forty boys before you, of ages from thirteen to sixteen, as they sit at their first botanical lesson; some curious to know what is going to happen, some resigned to anything; some convinced that it is all folly. You hand round to each boy several specimens, say of the Herb Robert; and taking one of the flowers, you ask one of them to describe the parts of it. 'Some pink leaves' is the reply. 'How many?' 'Five'. 'Any other parts?' 'Some little things inside'. 'Anything outside?' 'Some green leaves'. 'How many?' 'Five'. 'Very good. Now pull off the five green leaves outside,

and lay them side by side; next pull off the five pink leaves, and lay them side by side: and now examine the little things inside. What do you find?' 'A lot of little stalks or things'. 'Pull them off and count them'. They find ten. Then show them the little dust-bags at the top, and finally the curiously constructed central column, and the carefully concealed seeds. By this time all are on the alert. Then we resume: the parts in that flower are, outer green envelope, inner coloured envelope, the little stalks with dust bags, and the central column with the seeds. Then you give them all wall flowers: and they are to write down what they find: and you go round and see what they write down. Probably some one has found six 'storks' inside his wall-flower, and you make him write on the black-board for the benefit of the class the curious discovery, charging them all to note any such accidental varieties in future; and you make them very minutely notice all the structure of the central column. Then you give them all the common pelargonium and treat it similarly; and by the end of the hour they have learnt one great lesson, the existence of the four floral whorls, though they have yet not heard the name."

Of particular interest is the use of simple language. Many of Henslow's colleagues expressed surprise at the scientific terms handled by his village botanists but the professor had been relentless here.[24] Wilson's Rugby boys appeared to be making remarkable progress without the technical jargon!

F. E. Kitchener left Rugby School for Newcastle-under-Lyme where he introduced the same methods of teaching botany into the grammar school there.

Taunton School similarly embarked on a course of botany based on the investigation of fresh material.[25] Whether the master, the Reverend W. Tuckwell, had discussed the matter with Henslow or Wilson, when they had addressed the British Association on the subject is not known but it is very likely to be the case. Certainly, Tuckwell in his own address to the Exeter meeting in 1869 showed how greatly he was influenced by Henslow's methods of teaching botany. The equipment for the subject should include, he asserted,

"Professor Oliver's book [this was based on Henslow's manuscripts], a knife, a lens, le Maout's book, Professor Babington's modification of the Henslow schedules [fewer hard words], a small deal board, botanical microscope, two dissecting needles, forceps, flower trays for holding 18 bottles, Fitch's diagrams designed by the Committee of Council and Dr. Azocet's models of plant and plant organs."

Taunton School had obviously adopted the subject in to the curriculum permanently and had developed a botanic garden to help with the supply of fresh specimens. Joseph Hooker of Kew assisted in the stocking of this and similar school botanic gardens at Marlborough, Clifton and Cheltenham.[26]

So by the time the Devonshire Commission reported on Scientific and Technical Instruction in 1874, Rugby, Marlborough, Taunton, Clifton College, Cheltenham and St Paul's were all teaching botany in the Henslow tradition. It is possible that Winchester and Charterhouse were doing likewise, for they were certainly using Professor Daniel Oliver's textbook with the boys[27] and this textbook was written on the basis of Henslow's own manuscript. The book, embodying the Henslow method of botany teaching was brought out in a second edition in 1880 with sales at 67,000 by 1900.

*   *   *

No small influence on schools was exerted by the examination boards of the day. It is therefore fascinating to trace the direct or indirect guidance of the professor effected through the syllabuses and school examinations of London and Cambridge Universities. Henslow's influence can also be traced in the botany examinations of medical men, and of the Science and Art Department and of the College of Preceptors.

From 1838, London University included botany as one of its optional subjects for the matriculation examination and although the number of candidates in the early days seems to have been small and the candidates mostly adult yet the examinations were remarkable in their inclusion of first hand study of fresh botanical material. Thus when T. H. Huxley recalled this examination in 1842 he recorded,[28]

> "I recollect finding myself at last with pen and paper before me and five other beings, all older than myself, at a long table . . .We stared at one another like strange cats in a garret, but at length the examiner (Ward) entered, and before us placed the paper and sundry plants."

In spite of the implication that the candidates on that day were mature, yet there is evidence of the occasional school entry. In 1853, Alexander Black of St Paul's School won a ten pound prize on the results of the examination as did a candidate from Needham Grammar School six years later and a candidate from the North London Collegiate School in 1863.[29] In the earlier years candidates were asked to classify the specimens provided but in 1856 there was a deliberate move to require a botanical description of them in the Henslow style. Indeed, Professor Lindley, of University College and a great friend of Professor Henslow wrote a helpful shilling book entitled "Descriptive Botany", published in 1858, which stated clearly in its introduction that

> "the examiners in Botany at the Universities of Cambridge and London [i.e. Lindley and Henslow] have decided upon making Botanical descriptions a principal feature of their examination papers."

How familiar is the content of the book which aimed at helping the student to investigate specimens in order to arrive at a technical description! The recommended tools of the trade were familiar too, namely "a sharp penknife and pocket lens". Thus, from 1856 when this descriptive approach featured in the London Matriculation until 1864 when the subject was temporarily withdrawn, scientific investigation was encouraged as part of botanical study for candidates preparing for the examinations.

For schools taking the junior Cambridge examinations, similar influences were brought to bear. Kitchener, earlier described as assisting Wilson at Rugby when botany was introduced there, set the junior papers for the Cambridge Board for many years. To assist candidates in their practical investigations he rather belatedly published *Naked-eye Botany* in 1892. The schedule method of study was clearly advocated in the book and the familiar "pair of mounting needles", "knife and handlens" were described as the main tools of investigation. Kitchener's work was well and truly on the Hitcham model.

The senior papers for Cambridge schools, as we have seen, included from 1856 the compulsory practical investigation of floral specimens. Lindley and Henslow were determined that their respective Universities should show the way. Reports of examiners subsequently hint, however, that some schools had done little to encourage practical investigation by their pupils whose performance in this part of the examination was a disappointing one.[30] The spirit of Henslow's teaching had been neglected by these schools in spite of outside encouragement.

The University of London initiated a General Examination for Women in 1869, seven years after Henslow's death, and it is interesting to note that the botany examination included a compulsory observational question. This examination was entered by girls studying botany at Cheltenham Ladies' College, Bedford College School, Queen's College, the Ladies' College Kendall, the High Schools at Bath and Nottingham and the Mount School, York.[31] The even later advent of the University's Preliminary Scientific Examinations and the Intermediate B.Sc. Examinations in 1875 also included botany of the Henslow pattern with the provision of floral specimens on the occasion of the examination. Notable nineteenth century grammar schools entering pupils for these London University examinations included Epsom College, Stonyhurst, Kingswood, Charterhouse, Cheltenham Grammar, St Paul's, the Mercers School, the High Schools at Newcastle-under-Lyme, Nottingham and Manchester, and the Sheffield Royal Grammar School.[31] A number of boys preparing for these examinations would have been intending medical students.

The influence of Henslow's botany teaching on medical education cannot be ignored. Joseph Hooker was perhaps the main advocate here. Although no teacher, Hooker was greatly in demand as an examiner of botany and spent a considerable amount of time perfecting the art. He was asked, through the Queen's Physician in Ordinary, to examine in botany the candidates for the medical service under the East India Company in

1854 and soon sought the advice of Henslow in the matter. Writing[32] to his father-in-law the following year, Hooker indicated his wish to encourage botany teaching on a scientific basis and asked for guidance in the matter—

"I wish very much you could afford half an hour to think over the subject of 'Botany as a branch of education and a means of mental culture specially adapted to the early education of Medical men', and send me a few notions on the subject. I am preparing a notice of the mode of conducting the Botanical Examinations for the E.I.C., and want to drive it into the heads of Medical men and students that it is not with the hope that the Botanical knowledge obtained will ever be the slightest direct advantage to the man in practice that it should be taught, but because a right elementary knowledge is necessary to the right understanding of the Pharmacopoeia, Hygiene, therapeutics, Mat. Med., etc, and especially because the mental training of a good elementary Botanical or Nat. Hist. course is the best means of becoming skilful in diagnosis of diseases and developing his ideas. I am, however, a bad hand at expressing my ideas in mental philosophy and yet would like to do it properly."

His examinations in botany, based on the Henslow pattern had already attracted Huxley's attention in connection with the Apothecaries' Company and Hooker justified his emphasis on observation and reasoning rather than memory in a letter[33] to Huxley describing the purpose of the examination,

"You may remark that I did not put one catch-question, or one that did not involve general principles. There was not a man amongst them that had not studied plants for himself. I had another object in my paper, which was the leading men to study plants rather than books. Everyone but Henslow thinks my questions dreadful because nobody thinks of them. You must remember that they had eight hours; and that my object was to give questions requiring *thought* rather than *memory*."

Hooker evidently persevered with his intended endeavour and introduced the Henslow type of practical examination for Medical Officers not only of the Indian Army but also the British Army and the Navy. Indeed he claimed to have been one of a small group "which produced most extensive and important reforms in the Medical Schools"—reforms which in the botany field were firmly based on Professor Henslow's teaching methods.

It seems that the querying Huxley must have come to recognise and approve the success of the Henslow/Hooker system of botany teaching and examining for he later, in 1875, persuaded Joseph Hooker to write the botany science primer for students taking Elementary Botany for the examinations of the Science and Art Department at South Kensington.

The newly established Science and Art Department had looked to T. H. Huxley at the Royal School of Mines to modernise the syllabuses and promote further the cause of science in the nation's schools. Huxley had appointed two demonstrators in his botany laboratories, William Thistleton Dyer and Sidney Vines, "who were to change the face of Botany in the next few years". So claims Gilmour[34] writing of British botanists. Of the earlier Victorian botanists he asserted,

> "Their eyes were strained towards far distant horizons, . . . they missed the important developments in anatomy, morphology and physiology that were taking place across the Channel and North Sea. It was the mission of Dyer and Vines at South Kensington under Huxley's leadership to spread these new ideas."

Certainly Vines and Dyer did introduce experimental work in plant physiology into the new syllabuses. European progress in photosynthesis and transpiration was now brought to the students' attention. Nevertheless, Huxley, seeking a textbook written specifically for students taking the Science and Art Department examinations in Elementary Botany, initiated in 1875, persuaded Sir Joseph Hooker of Kew to write this botany science primer.[35] Thus Hooker was enabled to perpetuate the investigatory methods of his late father-in-law and incorporate them in an up-dated scientific syllabus. This of course, he gladly did. Observational exercises were included in his textbook and, from the start, a compulsory question in the Elementary Botany examination was the now familiar description of a fresh floral specimen and assignment to its Natural Order!

Of course many of the early candidates for the Science and Art Department examinations in botany were not school children[36] though a fair number, like Mr Lewisham in Wells' *Love and Mr Lewisham*, were destined to teach in our schools, carrying their newly learned scientific knowledge and methods with them. The Department's plan for teaching science, including botany, was adopted by some Higher Grade Schools, Organised Science Classes and other schools as the Annual Reports of the Department show. The Church of St Saviour's School, Birmingham and Bedford Commercial School were early participants in the botany scheme.[37] Further, A. A. Mumford in his history of Manchester Grammar School claims their use of the Science and Art Department plan from 1874 even though the scheme faltered for a while through lack of a practical examiner.[38]

Throughout the country were a number of private and proprietary schools. The latter were set up to serve groups of children whose parents had common interests and were prepared to finance their children's modest education. Towards the end of the century many of these schools looked to the College of Preceptors to assess their standards of achievement. For these schools, Professor George Henslow, botanist son of the Hitcham rector, acted as examiner in botany and clearly he did what he could to uphold the tradition of his father's botany teaching methods.

Difficulties were great, however, for the urban schools had no regular supply of fresh specimens and this type of school had neither the rich endowments of the Public Schools nor the land to allow development of a botanic garden. Only at the turn of the century when Kew Gardens, Hyde Park and Richmond Park ran a supply service for schools in the London area did the situation ease for schools here. Elsewhere, the problems remained. Nevertheless, George Henslow pursued his mission relentlessly and, as late as 1885, a practical question was at last included in the botany examination. The following year the children were asked to give a scientific description of the provided floral specimen[39]—in the Henslow manner. George Henslow's slim textbook *Botany for Children*, published 1880, consisted of a series of descriptions of common plants and, predictably, a guide to further descriptions to be made by the children themselves.

Thus, during the second half of the nineteenth century botany was accepted into many different English schools. Henslow's influence was firmly stamped on the methods of teaching generally employed. It is, however, ironical that least provision for the subject was made in the nation's elementary schools and it was primarily for the scientific education of these children of "the labouring classes" that Henslow's Hitcham scheme for school botany had been devised.

CHAPTER SIX

Adult Education in the Village—
Exhibitions and Expeditions

HENSLOW certainly did not neglect the education of the adult members of his community and used his talents and ingenuity both to introduce his parishioners to the methods and applications of science in agriculture and to expand their general education.

His work must be seen against a background of agricultural development of the time.[1] "Practice with Science" was the motto adopted by the Royal Agricultural Society established in 1838 and it summarised the spirit behind the movement to rescue British farming from the agricultural depression bedevilling the early decades of the century. Generally adverse climatic conditions had led to the abandonment of heavy soil; rot had led to the killing of many sheep; and, more relevant to Suffolk, blight had taken a heavy toll of the crops. Further, an urgent need to intensify agricultural production was later made more pressing by the repeal of the Corn Laws in 1846. Hope stemmed from developments in agricultural science. Work on artificial manures was gaining momentum and making an impact on farming methods. In Germany, Justice Leibig published his work on *Organic Chemistry and Its Application to Agriculture and Physiology* in 1840. An English edition was prepared by Lyon Playfair and was received with enthusiasm in Britain. Henslow deemed it a very important contribution to agricultural advance. In this country, in 1843, Joseph Lawes opened Rothamstead Experimental Station where experimental horticultural trials were to take place.

Suffolk, in which the village of Hitcham lay, had not been so badly hit as other areas with heavier soils but farming methods were unenlightened. A Board of Agriculture survey at the turn of the century[2] showed that even the effective rotation of crops had been ignored and that grain yields were low. Certainly, there was much unemployment amongst the labouring class.

Such was the situation when Henslow arrived in Hitcham in 1837 and it was not surprising that as a man of science, as well as a social reformer, he should tackle the problem from the educational and scientific angle as well as the humanitarian one.

Henslow saw the fundamental challenge to lie in the introduction of better husbandry based on scientific farming. To this end he sought to educate both the labouring classes and farmers alike and pursued his task with the thoroughness and purpose of the skilled scientist and teacher that he was. His methods of approach to the two classes were of course totally different but his aim was commonly the betterment of the land. With regard to the agricultural labourers, Henslow's genial approach to them was recorded in a contemporary journal[3]—

> "the first step was to attach the 'labouring class' to himself, and induce them to regard him as a friend; for this purpose, being a capital pyrotechnist, he invited them to the Rectory lawn in the evening and amused them with fireworks, and then gradually introduced to their notice many simple objects of domestic use hitherto unknown to them, and having once gained their confidence he lost no time in setting to work on a plan that should tell at once on the bodies and minds of the labourers."

Further, an early introduction of popular village ploughing matches aimed at giving labourers an interest in their work and at developing a pride in good husbandry. 1838 saw the first of these matches which were pursued enthusiastically by the labourers and it seems that they continued in Hitcham at least until 1851. It is doubtful whether they would have ended then were it not for the opposition of farmers who could not bear their own men to perform less well than another's. Thus, it is recorded[4] that

> "In 1838 ploughing matches were introduced, and applauded by the labourers; it might have been supposed by the farmers too; but with characteristic obstructiveness they for many years continued to throw in the apple of discord and rendered fair play impossible."

It is important to realise that these farmers had demoralised the previous incumbent by opposing his attempts to reform, but they were clearly unable to deter Henslow in his determination to better the lot of his parishioners and of improving the use of the land. He realised that he must fight the battle with the farmers on a different front and in a different way. His tactics are described later.

For the labourers he also introduced an allotment scheme such as had succeeded in neighbouring villages. In 1845 he published an *Address to landlords on the advantages to be expected from the general establishment of a spade tenantry among the labouring classes.*[5] In this he outlined the social arguments for improving the farm labourers' conditions and in this way justified the allotment scheme and quoted practical examples of successful schemes already operating at Walsham le Willows and at Barton in his own county. The latter was held up as a model for Hitcham. Sir H. Bunbury had there allotted half an acre sites as near as possible to the labourers' own cottages.

The *Bury and Norwich Post* had given publicity to his vigorous campaign by publishing a series of letters "To the Public" and "To the Landlords of Suffolk". In them he admitted that the "allotment system presents itself rather as an act of grace than of justice", but he maintained that, nevertheless, the system had economic justifications. He wrote to the landlords,[6] in November, 1844,

> "Surely it is by using every exertion to increase the produce of your own soil that the agriculture of England can alone expect to be for ever able to keep out the corn from Canada and from elsewhere."

While the editor gave Henslow fair space from 27th October to 20th November for his campaign, he disclaimed any personal backing for the professor's views, adding that he favoured a "Land Improvement Society" as existed in Yorkshire. Indeed, Henslow pursued this particular campaign with even less support than he usually could muster but with no less determination. Even his family expressed their doubts and he confessed in a November letter "To the Public"[7] that his brother,

> "well-acquainted with my natural disposition has written to say that he is ashamed at the tones of my first address and fears that the public will think me presumptuous and egotistical."

The campaign continued unrelentingly however and eventually with grudging success. The first two allotments were within the fields of the glebe.[8] When the Hitcham Charity Land became available again in 1849, Henslow was able to secure 16 acres for 8 years and it was this land that he allocated as ¼-acre allotments. The farmers had not relented and continued to make it very difficult for Henslow. Thus, when he acquired 20 more acres the following year, some of the allottees had to withdraw their names because the farmers "by whom they were pretty generally employed, would not allow them to hold an allotment under the pain and penalty of being refused further employment on their farms".

Henslow's brother-in-law, Jenyns, reported that in his own Cambridgeshire parish he too had run into farmer opposition to an allotment scheme on the grounds that "the men would give their masters short time and easy work" to reserve their energies for allotment work later in the day! Allegations of stealing the masters' seed were also made. In Hitcham, however, the opposition was much stronger and based on social fears.[9] Jenyns explained that

> ". . . the farmers are apt to think that the holding of an allotment will give the labourer a spirit of independence that will interfere with the service he owes his master."

Henslow persisted, however, and the scheme developed as a practical basis on which he could eventually introduce the labourers to a little of the science of farming.

Encouragement came largely from the rector's faithful friends. Charles Darwin, for example, writing to Henslow regretting his own absence from a British Association meeting in Birmingham in September 1849, included approval of the Hitcham allotment scheme in the text of the letter.[10]

"Your Allotment scheme seems an excellent one: how active you always seem to be with your many plans of doing good to your Parish."

Mr Ransome, of the famous ironworks of Ipswich, sent the allottees three dozen whetstones; a "gentleman" sent thirty-five sorts of vegetable seed and three kinds of flower seed; and Professor Lindley, Henslow's colleague and loyal friend, furnished the cottagers with imported guano, a highly effective manure containing phosphate of lime and recently discovered in Chile. Locally, too, he had the support of at least one farmer who was prepared to cart loads of manure free to the Hitcham plots.

With this limited but practical encouragement Henslow was able to foster the scheme and encourage the labourers to develop scientific ways of cultivating the land. The men were able to exhibit their produce at the Hitcham horticultural shows held twice a year from 1850 onwards and to compete for prizes given by the rector, his family and his friends.[11] But these shows were much more than exhibitions of flowers and vegetables, Henslow immediately seized the opportunity to mould them into educational events.

"A more intellectual rural fete cannot be conceived. It is true that the people of Hitcham have a leader of rare gifts and high attainment . . ."

wrote an eyewitness of the 1857 show in the *Gardeners' Chronicle*[12] of that year.

The shows certainly had educational content but they were anything but dull. They were extremely well attended by members of the Hitcham Labourers' and Mechanics' Horticultural Society and their families who enjoyed the side-shows, sports, marquee museum and superb teas! The handbill[13] of the 1851 July show is reproduced here to illustrate the rich variety of activity in the rectory grounds. It outlines the regular features of the Hitcham shows. Prizes were given to the allottees and to the village botanists; the rector delivered at least one lecture; the marquee museum included attractive exhibits[14] and the tea in the tent concluded proceedings, save for the National Anthem—

"Hitcham Labourers' and Mechanics' Horticultural Society
Wednesday, July 16th, 1851

All specimens to compete for prizes must be at the Rectory before half past 10 o'clock; to allow time for their being arranged and inspected by Judges. Children competing for Wild-flower Nosegays must bring their flowers before nine and make up their nosegays under the Horse-chestnut trees near the house.

At 2 o'clock any persons desirous of seeing the show may come on the lawn and amuse themselves. Those who prefer a game of cricket may adjourn to a neighbouring field.

Various specimens will be exhibited to illustrate the uses to which 'Woody Fibre' may be put, at 4 o'clock Mr Henslow will make a few remarks on this subject. Numerous plates and woodcrafts chiefly relating to the Crystal Palace and the articles in it will also be exhibited; and a selection of Natural History objects will be shown with the above.

At 5 o'clock the prizes will be announced and distributed.

At 6 o'clock six stewards will arrange the members of the Horticultural Society who are inclined to take a sociable cup of tea altogether and see that they are properly attended to.

At 8 o'clock the last notes of God Save the Queen, by the Semer House (local orphanage) band will have informed the company that it is time for all loyal subjects to return home; and Mr Henslow will then repeat his thanks for the orderly behaviour and good conduct which he well knows by past experience will have characterised 'the proceedings' of the day."

There is no doubt that the event was a success although some of the enthusiastic yokels had broken through the hedges[15] in their excitement. The October show followed with an emphasis on flower rather than the earlier vegetable production. Henslow seems to have been well pleased with the level of cultivation that year and writes to Thomas Martin, surgeon friend and founder of Reading's Mechanics' Institute, about the exhibits.[16]

"Hitcham
2nd October 1851

My dear Sir,

I enclose a programme of our Horticultural Society meeting yesterday —the show up to the distribution of prizes was favoured by the weather—but the day wound up with heavy rain—which however was not for much consequence to those (196) who were seated under a booth at tea. We had a capital exhibition of Wheat, Potatoes etc. Also 14 out of 17 exhibited for Baine's Dahlia very well grown flowers—and some of the best Asters (the judges said) they had ever seen in a Village or at many Horticultural shows.—I was obliged by the weather to postpone my little lecture.

Yours very truly,
J. S. HENSLOW."

Little wonder that these delightful and educative shows captured the nation's interest! The 1853 July event was reported fully by Henslow's conchologist friend, Lovell Reeve, in the July *Literary Gazette* and an extract reprinted from the famous botanical journal *Proceedings of the Linnean Society*.[17] It recaptured the fascination of the hour in lighthearted terms.

". . . Opposite . . . are arranged the fuschias, geraniums, roses, pinks, stocks, pansies, annuals and perennials, nosegays and device nosegays, and at the end the rustics are peeping with astonishment into a polyorama and a stereoscope. On the opposite side of the green is a tent devoted to general curiosities. Eggs of alligators, and eggs of ostrich, eggs of humming-birds, and eggs of some other wonderful birds incubating lilliputian cottages in yolk of shells and moss, casts of Echini in their flinty matrices and Echini in chalk, vegetable ivory, from the nut to its process of turning into pin-cushions and umbrella handles, ammonites and nautili, bright enamelled shells of all kinds, butterflies and scorpions, grasses and sedges, lace book and chocolate in the pod; but it is beyond our memory to enumerate the specimens of this instructive museum, all set out and stored away again in one day by the busy Professor in his St. Alban's hat of plaited straw."

Only paid-up members of the Hitcham Labourers' and Mechanics' Horticultural Society could attend and enter their produce for the prizes generously given at the shows. Competition was keen but friendly. The same observer related—

"The ruling principle of the Hitcham Labourers' and Mechanics' Horticultural Society, is that every member should feel his independence as a contributing subscriber. They are of the very poorest class. Few, very few alas! of the parents are able to read and write. The subscription is *sixpence per annum*, and out of this small fund two shows—one of flowers and one of vegetables—are held with great rejoicing in the grounds of the rectory. Prizes varying from 2s 6d to a pinch of white snuff—i.e. peppermint lozenges—are offered by the rector, gentry and farmers, to the most successful cultivators, and the award of the judges looked forward to each year with as much competing excitement as the gold and silver Banksian and Knightsian Medals of the metropolis."

The award of prizes was clearly an important feature of the shows and the reporter rightly emphasised this. He understated the usefulness of many of these prizes (tools, fertilizers, barometer, teapot) and clearly could not have realised a further importance attached to the donations. Henslow's generous and influential friends became "involved" in the shows and their support greatly assisted him to sustain the allotment scheme and make it a success in face of farmer opposition.

In October 1851, the handbill for the Hitcham show announced Professor Lindley's interest in the venture.

"4 p.m. Prizes distributed, including some pure guano placed at the disposal of the judges by Dr. Lindley the celebrated Botanist."

But Lindley's assistance by no means ended with the supply of guano. As editor of the horticultural section of the *Gardeners' Chronicle* he gave generous space to eye witness accounts of the shows over the years. He understood Henslow's underlying concern for improved cultivation of the land and the token award of guano at that early October show was followed by further supplies and consideration of its use. Responding to Henslow's request in 1856 he replied[18] sympathetically from Acton Green on 27th October,

". . . I don't think you can get so small a quantity of real Guano as 11 lbs off the dealers. Luckily I have just bought 2 cwt. and will give your allottees that quantity. Only tell me whether to send it to you directly or to keep it here for you."

And, in an undated letter from the Horticultural Society, London, he gave some advice to Henslow on how a cottager can use guano best. He later visited Hitcham, observed the progress of the scheme of allotments and wrote[19] with admiration—

"Your prosperity in the Cottager line is such as to be the admiration of all earnest men and the despair of all dolts and sluggards."

In 1859, Lindley distributed the prizes at the vegetable show himself. Writing subsequently in his journal about this occasion, he praised Henslow's "tact in organisation" and advocated that "anyone interested should visit Hitcham and learn". More importantly perhaps, he recorded the high standard of cultivation witnessed at the village allotments.[20] This was, of course, one of the major aims of the allotment scheme.

"It is the practice at Hitcham, twice in the season, to inspect the cottagers' allotments and to award some gardening implements to the owners of those best cultivated. Here too the improvement is steady and marked, year by year the inspectors find less fault, while the best are like neatly kept gardens. The first prize man had 46 crops on his allotment, yet of this variety none were neglected, as was proved by his also taking 10 prizes for different articles."

Bree of Ipswich, with whom Henslow corresponded[21] on scientific and educational matters, also supplied prizes from the early days of the allotment competitions. Henslow wrote on 22nd July, 1851 acknowledging Bree's generosity,

". . . Many thanks for the trouble you took about prizes—Is it likely that another year the Stowmarket Society would allow some of our allottees to compete for their prizes for good cultivation? . . ."

Nothing apparently came of the suggested Stowmarket co-operation but records show that the Bree family continued their interest in the Hitcham events contributing more prizes to later shows[22] (including the then traditional "teapot" and "barometer"). More than this, the Bree family appear to have attended the fetes. A letter[23] to Bree written on 10th October, 1853, expresses Henslow's concern that Mrs Bree "suffered no ill effects from standing so long in the tent". He then responded humbly to

Bree's kind praise of the show (printed as one of a series of reports in the *Gardeners' Chronicle*),

> "you really have patted me on the back in the *Gardeners' Chronicle* in a manner that might make me vain if I had not learnt to know that kind friends are want to see with magnifiers . . ."

Nor was Knights, the curator of Ipswich Museum and friend of Henslow its president, left unaware of the Hitcham Horticultural shows. Materials from the museum augmented Henslow's own collections for exhibition in the famous rectory marquee museums. In July 1855, Henslow assured Knights in a letter[24] that

> "the museum was a greater source of attention than ever.
> I managed to deliver two lectures, spite my hoarseness, which were well attended!!"

The following July, Knights had evidently produced livestock for the show and the extract from the letter of acknowledgement[25] incidentally revealed the strain these village shows imposed on the professor personally.

> "Many thanks for the Fish. I have been unable to reply earlier—One died but the other four, two looking a little sickly from their journey, will I think thrive. They excited a good deal of Village attention—tho' the wet kept away most of our distant friends, we had a good muster of Villagers and the afternoon was fine enough. Above 300 sat down to tea—I gave 5 courses of lectures to a crowded audience and got thoroughly tired. I was not at all in fit condition of brain or voice for responding to a toast assigned to my care at the Chelmsford dinner next day . . ."

Knights, too, had been drawn into the spirit of these endeavours and it is not surprising to read in Lindley's account of the 1859 autumn show[26] that it was Knights who had contributed the traditional "teapot" to the prize list that year.

Alas, the following season saw the last of Hitcham's Horticultural Shows on Henslow's rectory lawn. The educational content of the final event is so remarkable for its breadth and intensity that the programme[27] is reproduced at length as a tribute to the professor's untiring devotion to the popular education and the betterment of his villagers. These shows had been presented with rich educational experience alongside all the fun of the fair.

Hitcham Labourers' and Mechanics' Horticultural Society.
Second Show, Oct. 3rd, 1860

"8 to 10 a.m.   Specimens received on the rectory lawn.

12   Marquee museum ready for inspection. Lecturets as opportunity offers later in the day. Among additions since the July Show observe

1. Five unpublished lithographic portraits of their Royal Highnesses, the Princesses Alice, 1859; Helena, 1849, Louise, 1851; and the Princes Arthur, 1859; Leopold, 1859.

2. Photographs of highly-magnified objects of Natural History; among which are a fly's tongue and eye; Parasites (lice) of Man and Ox; Spider's claws; Saws of a Saw fly; fossil Foraminifera. N.B. The Chalk (in round numbers, 1000 miles in length, 500 in breadth, and 1000 feet thick,) has been mainly produced by these microscopic creatures! Section of Pinewood with circular disks on the cells.

3. Magnified representations of 151 forms of Snow Crystals.

4. Case containing living specimens of our smallest British Mammal, the Harvest Mouse.

5. Pearls from four British Mollusks, viz., Oyster, Periwinkle, Pearl-muscle, Freshwater Clam.

6. For the sake of Children, young and old. A case containing a "Heap" of Shells and Corals; also, under a Glass shade, a new Device from the last Horticultural Show in "Fairly-land."

1 p.m.	Show-booth ready for inspection.
2½	Prizes to Village Botanists of the first class, for (1) Wild-fruit Posies; (2) Dried-grass Posies. N.B. The species to be named in each case. (3) Herbarium specimens. School Report.
3	Allotment Report. Prizes distributed for (1) Superior Culture; (2) Hatcher Sweepstakes; (3) Specimens exhibited at this Show. Thanks to the Judges, Donors of Prizes, and all others aiding and abetting our proceedings.
4	Begin to remove Specimens from the Booth. Not to forget to restore Cheque and Prize Tickets to the Stewards.
5	Ready for Tea. Ticketless Babies (0 to 2 years old) and Ticketed Ditto (2 to 4 years) admitted as heretofore.
6	God save the Queen. Good Night. May the occasion prove a blessing, without a single instance of offence against the laws of God or Man."

*   *   *

Yet another way in which Henslow sought to improve the education of his adult villagers was by opening his well-stocked library of over 100 books to the parishioners in 1840.[28] The library was open for all classes of the community and he provided a lending library for schoolchildren, farmers, friends and others in the neighbourhood. He registered it as a Parish Charity in 1841 and recorded in the parish accounts of that year that most of the books were in constant circulation amongst members of the community. Writing in the *Bury and Norwich Post* three years later on the subject of lending libraries, Henslow noted the limitations of libraries available in the villages. He pointed out that books were borrowed mostly by schoolchildren who were almost the only persons of their class who could read.[29] Henslow faced up to this challenge and the handicap of the adult non-reader was not left unattended for long in Hitcham village. Adult literacy classes for young women were started by Easter of 1849[30] with Henslow's daughter as tutor. By 1858, the classes were regularised and in his Easter sermon Henslow recorded "One Adult Class for young women, (on Monday afternoon) and two for young men (on Tuesday and Thursday evening) during five months of the year had been carried on under the direction of Miss Henslow and my Curate, the Rev. R. D. Graves".[31] It appears that about 17 men and 14 women students were involved in these classes the following year[32] and it is almost certain that they were devoted largely to the teaching of reading. Henslow's son George was later brought in to assist. The pence paid by the adult pupils covered most of the expenses but the coals for heating and the candles were given as a charity. That the students did not find it any too easy to learn at a mature age was a fact which Henslow emphasised in an undated Easter week sermon[33] seeking support for his parish school,

"parents should remember that unless their children master the rudiments of learning when young, the difficulty of doing so is greatly increased to them in later life."

The list of books available at Hitcham library[34] makes it clear that apart from some travel volumes and village scrap books there was little light reading! A few of the titles are listed here.

Penny Magazine	12 volumes
Milford's Greece	10 volumes
Hook's Rome	12 volumes
Gibbon's Rome	12 volumes
Fitton's Geology of Hastings	
Richardson's Geology	
Lyell's Geology	4 volumes
Roget's Bridgwater Treatise[35]	2 volumes

A contemporary document[36] claims that Henslow was most generous with his loan collection which,

". . . is not confined to the Parish of Hitcham and nothing gives him greater pleasure than to supply *all* that can apply for *any*, he has told me that they (the books) can answer no practical good to remain on the shelves".

*   *   *

The contents of his library may have been out of the intellectual reach of most of the parishioners but he found other active, entertaining and more acceptable ways of broadening their education. From the summer of 1848 he set out annually from Hitcham with a happy and well organised band of his villagers to explore, in one day, some new part of East Anglia opened up by the new network of railways. The first of the excursions was to Ipswich. Few of the villagers had previously travelled by rail and George Henslow remembers the excitement of their first journey.[37]

"This novelty was, therefore, at first an important part of the trip, not to mention passing through the tunnel at Ipswich, which caused an occasion for excitement, resulting in much whistling and shouting."

At Ipswich itself, the Ransome family were most helpful in showing the astonished rural visitors round their famous ironworks.[38] The success of the outing led to a repeat the following year with an imaginative addition to the programme—a trip on the *River Queen* steamer down to Harwich. It is not surprising that the numbers clamouring to come on the second excursion were higher than before. Henslow was determined to control the membership and thence the conduct of the second and extended expedition with the same success as the experimental one the year before.

"All who has been of the first party were now invited, each with permission to nominate a companion. I retained a veto in issuing tickets, but found no occasion to exercise it in any case where application was made to me according to the prescribed rule."

It is interesting to learn from Henslow's account that some of the farmers considered the outing decorous enough to join the party.

"We were joined on this occasion by several of the farmers to whom the good conduct of the party on the previous year had been reported. Our party now had reached to 180 including members of my own family, and all my servants."

Only a few farmers joined the expedition in these early days although others were unable to resist them in later years. Henslow's son George recorded that from the beginning some of them helped to transport the travellers as far as Stowmarket by loaning their waggons for the day.[39] An invitation was extended to them to participate and/or assist as can be seen in the general announcement of the 1849 excursion.[40]

"The Hitcham members of the Stoke and Melford Benefit Society with their friends, are invited by members of the Ipswich Museum and of the Young Men's Association of Ipswich to take part in an excursion on the 'River Queen' steamer down to Harwich on Wednesday, July 25th. The following arrangements under Mr. Henslow's superintendence are appointed for organising the party and maintaining order.

THE PARTY TO CONSIST OF:

(1) Any resident Hitcham member of the Stoke and Melford Society.
(2) Such friends of the above as joined the party to Ipswich last year.
(3) Every Hitcham member of the Stoke and Melford Society to be at liberty to name one friend in addition to those who joined the party last year.

Any of the farmers of Hitcham who may be willing to promote this description of recreation, are invited to join with some of Mr. Henslow's family who propose to accompany the excursion. Tickets for the excursion may be procured at the Rectory on the payment of one shilling and six pence which is to include all the expenses of travelling and refreshment. Refreshments to consist of tea and coffee, lemonade, bread, cheese, butter and plum cake.

Hitcham Rectory.
14th July 1849.

Mr. Henslow *suggests* either loan of waggon or 1/- subscription toward keep of horses at Stowmarket."

Evidently the Harwich outing was a great success and an Ipswich newspaper printed on the 31st July, carried a favourable local report[41] entitled "A Trip to Harwich".

"On Wednesday last a party of friends and parishioners of Professor Henslow, accompanied by the respected Professor himself, paid a visit to the Committee of Ipswich Museum and Young Men's Association. In order to make this visit as much of a holiday as possible, and to provide the Hitcham party with just those objects of interest which they could least procure at home, the 'River Queen' was engaged for the occasion and a steam upon the river, a call at Harwich, and a stroll over the grounds of J. Bagshaw, Esquire, at Dovercourt, who kindly opened them to the party, was the pro-gramme of the day—about 10 o'clock the main division of the party arrived by rail from Stowmarket, shortly after followed by the Semer band from Hadleigh. Owing to the kind exertions of Mr. Daking, the wharf belonging to the Ipswich Steam Navigation Company was converted into a comfortable breakfast apartment. The 'River Queen' took the party aboard a little after 11 o'clock, the Mr. Humfress and Semer Juveniles adding considerably to the enjoyment of the trip.

After strolling through Harwich, examining the fort, etc., which was kindly exhibited by Mr. Sharpe, and partaking of luncheon at Dovercourt, the signal for return was given, and the steamer arrived at the Griffin Strait just one minute before the time for departure for the train. Doubtless it will be a day long to be remembered by the good people of Hitcham—an event for many years to be chronicled amongst the recollection of 'Our Village'.

The utmost good feeling and order was manifest throughout the day's proceedings and every heart apparently beat happily. Perhaps there was too much of the 'move on' spirit of the age in so extended excursion, and a few hours quiet lounge on the cliffs of Harwich might have been so much additional pleasure; but on the whole it was one of those delightful occurrences, which, whilst scattering happiness abroad, tends also to bind society together in the bonds of unity."

Whatever the outside observers may have thought of this expedition, Henslow's greatest joy was "seeing labourers encounter their first dogrose" —thus confessed the botanist in a letter[42] (probably to Thomas Martin in Reading) on 7th August, 1849. This letter, a general one relating the pressure of parish work concerning weddings (and early births thereafter!), strongly emphasised Henslow's concern for proper organisation of the village outings, for firm rules and for the co-operation of all involved. The printed regulations for the 1850 excursion revealed even tighter controls. They were expressed in good-humoured terms[43]:—

"HITCHAM EXCURSION TO IPSWICH AND LANDGUARD FORT, ON TUESDAY, 30th JULY, 1850.

I. According to my expressed determination last year, I am making arrangements for a village excursion to Ipswich and Landguard Fort; having received assurances that we shall be welcome at both those places.

II. The successful issue of such an excursion (provided no untoward accident should occur) will mainly depend upon a general attention to a few rules, which I here propose to those who wish to accompany me.

III. Every one is to be in good humour, accommodating towards all, and especially attentive to the ladies of the party. If the weather should prove unpropitious, every one is to make the best of it, and not to complain more than he can possibly help.

IV. Those who are invited on the present occasion are the occupiers of farms in Hitcham, the resident members of the Stoke and Melford Club, and those who attend the adult class on Saturdays. Every one who joins the party may also name a friend, residing in Hitcham, for whose good conduct he will be responsible.

V. The tickets to be issued will be limited to 200, at 1s 6d. each. All applications to be made at the Rectory on or before Friday the 26th. Should any tickets remain unapplied for after that day by the parties invited, those who have already received tickets may apply for more for other friends. By this arrangement I hope to accommodate all, or nearly all, who may be wishing to take part in the excursion.

VI. The party are to assemble on the platform at Stowmarket by half-past eight.

VII. As the object of the party is not to be mere eating and drinking, but wholesome recreation to body and mind, the refreshments provided will consist of bread, cheese, butter, cake, with lemonade, and one or two pints of beer for those who may apply for an order to that effect when they receive their tickets. These orders for beer are not to be transferred to other parties; and if not needed are to be returned.

VIII. Should any one be prevented at the last moment from joining the party, 1s of the money paid will be returned; and the remaining 6d will be appropriated towards the expenses that will have been incurred, upon the supposition that such person would have been of the party.

IX. Every one must contrive for himself how to get from Hitcham to Stowmarket, and back again. If he is not able to persuade any one to give him a lift, he must consent (as others have done before) to wear out a little shoe-leather.

J. S. HENSLOW.''

There is no doubt that Henslow's insistence on good behaviour was effective and even the fastidious magistrate Dr Clarke, whose loathing of the "vile" public caused him to resign from his curatorship of Ipswich Museum in 1851, praised the conduct of the Hitcham visitors.[44]

"When Professor Henslow's parties of neatly and respectably dressed people came from Hitcham what a contrast they present to the vile disorderly mob that contaminate our Room on 'public nights'."

The excursions were noteworthy in many ways not least in opening the eyes of the villagers to new experiences. Henslow's son recalled, for example, the villagers' amazement at the sight of the sea.[45]

"Immediately a rush is made for the shore; pebbles, seaweed, bottles of salt water are carried off as mementoes."

Professor Henslow, himself gave a more cautious account[46] which highlighted the reactions—often those of apprehension—to the new experiences provided by the 1850 excursion.

"The party were not prepared for all they had to expect. Scarcely any of them had seen the sea, or been in a boat. Dread of water was a predominant feeling and some of the more fainthearted had staid at home from this cause, though longing to join us. Even the railway was a novelty to several and there was much whistling and shouting provoked on immerging into the darkness of the tunnel."

After breakfast prepared by the Ipswich Y.M.C.A. in a cleared warehouse, the party boarded a flag-decked boat by plank. This caused considerable trepidation for some. The trip itself brought challenging experiences and Henslow recorded that one girl, viewing with puzzlement the foam on the river water arising from the steampaddle, asked him "Is it hot water?"

George, the professor's son, recalled[47] the delight given to the party after it had landed at Landguard Fort. The officer in command, he recalled,

> "volunteered to exercise the artillery in a variety of field movements, drill and gunnery practice, for the amusement of the villagers; who were conducted through the forest, while several joined the privates at cricket and football".

But apparently Henslow's labourers were not greeted everywhere with the civility extended them at Ipswich, Harwich and Landguard Fort that July. When the party reached Stowmarket it seems to have borne the brunt of a political demonstration by free traders against protectionists. Thus, before going to Norwich in the following year Henslow wrote to his friend Bree[48] explaining that he would again be passing through Stowmarket and expressing the hope that the blackguards of that town would be more civil to the countrymen than previously. Evidently, clods and stones had been thrown at them by the group of free traders and, Henslow observed,

> "though some of us *are* protectionists, there are some that are *not*, and I don't suppose your free traders can distinguish at a glance which is which".

Further expeditions took place without incident and Henslow's kind friends continued to assist him where they could.

The professor had, however, annoyed the farmers of the area once again by deciding to subsidise these village excursions from money previously used for their annual tithe dinners—"frolics" of about forty farmers where there had been excessive drinking by some. Henslow, describing "radical reform in part of our village economics"[49] claimed characteristically that he was loathe to inhibit his flock from meeting socially and was proposing a more valuable social enterprise—the annual excursion.

> "I was unwilling to abandon an old custom which (however abused) afforded us opportunity of meeting in friendly intercourse. It now occurred to me that I could procure this object in a far better manner by appropriating the sum these unsatisfactory 'frolics' cost me, towards a fund for carrying out such excursions as double experience had proved grateful to those who had tried them."

He further added that, unlike the behaviour of some at the tithe dinners, the behaviour of individuals on excursions was easy to control.

"Where the maximum allowance is two pints of beer (diluted with a sufficiency of milder potations) there is no risk of intemperance even with those whose throats are least under self-control."

It took four or five years to win back the support of the farmers to this particular cause but the expeditions continued successfully, nevertheless.

The preparatory notice of the 1851 Norwich outing re-emphasised the need to ensure the good behaviour of all taking part in the excursion. This and other information was contained in a postscript to a handbill[50] of the Hitcham Labourers' and Mechanics' Horticultural Society, 16th July, 1851—

Mr. Henslow is making preparations for a village excursion to Norwich on Tuesday, 22nd July, some gentlemen of that city have most kindly tendered their assistance in procuring rooms for the reception of the party, for viewing the cathedral, and a large establishment for the manufacture of shawls, and other places of interest.

200 tickets (one shilling each) are prepared for this excursion. They may be procured before Saturday, the 19th, at the Rectory, by the farmers, the Hitcham members of the Stoke and Melford Society, and the members of the Horticultural Society. If there should be any not called for by that time, they may be obtained by those who have already taken tickets for friends residing in Hitcham, for whose good behaviour they can be responsible."

The hospitality was generous indeed with Mr Blakesly, Mayor, providing several rounds of beef and hot plum puddings in St Andrews Hall. During the meal the organist played to the party and then accompanied them as they sang the Evening Hymn and National Anthem.[51]

That same year Henslow took a small party of twenty villagers to London for three days on a visit to the Great Exhibition, the Zoological Gardens, the Polytechnic and the Gardens at Kew.[52] George Henslow recounts that friends helped make the expensive trip possible. The party were given free entry to the zoo; a stranger paid for the party's admission to the Polytechnic; and relations (presumably his daughter and son-in-law, Joseph Hooker) funded the Kew visit.[53]

Further excursions were organised with help from his family and friends. The local farmers remained generally sceptical, however, until the professor devised an expedition to his dear Cambridge in 1854. They were captivated by his plans for that day and could hold out against him no longer. They added their names to the list of participants and received schedules of places to visit and things to see prepared in detail by Henslow himself.[54] Amongst these places of interest was included the botanical gardens which Henslow had spent so much time and energy developing over his years at Cambridge. A full plan was provided for the visitors and his old student C. C. Babington showed "The respectably dressed strangers" around "under Henslow's orders".[55]

No less a person than the Vice-Chancellor gave them lunch at Downing Hall of the University with "ample plum pudding and beer provided for all". Good will was generated all round. That Henslow was pleased with the expedition can be detected clearly from the cheerful letter[56] to his friend, Knights, on the 31st July of that year,

> "our Cambridge trip turned out a perfect success—I have not heard a single murmur and all seem to have been unusually delighted. I will bring you a programme I had printed for the occasion and illustrated. We had a large body of farm men, and for the first time the Baptist dissenters of their party joined us. We sat down 283 to dinner."

This recorded a resounding social victory for Henslow as well as testimony to a first-rate educational excursion to be repeated in the following year. The outing had broken across class and religious barriers within the parish. Not only had Baptist dissenters joined the party for the first time but farmers were well represented. Indeed, George Henslow later claimed that these erstwhile sceptical and critical men were so delighted that they could no longer hide their admiration for the professor and presented him with a silver cup in thanks for the Cambridge excursion which they had so greatly enjoyed and appreciated.[57]

These highly organised and inspiring excursions ran for eight successful years until, in 1857, increased prices and new railway regulations made them no longer feasible.[58] The social and educational impact of the expeditions on the Hitcham parishioners is incalculable but there is no doubt that they must have awakened the minds of those villagers to events and ways of life far beyond their parish bounds.

CHAPTER SEVEN

Science and the Farmers

THE farmers of Hitcham parish had dominated and intimidated the previous incumbent and they were prepared to treat Henslow in like manner. From his early years at the parish Henslow was aware of their strong opposition to any proposed reform which might improve the lot of the villagers. Ploughing matches, allotment schemes, the parish school had all been opposed. Henslow's fiery and passionate sermons and addresses on matters of social justice had left the farmers unmoved and his appeals for financial aid for the school and other charities had gone unheeded. Jenyns recorded that Hitcham farmers "held their men in grievous subjection" and in their attitudes to reform showed "obstinacy and prejudice".[1]

But Henslow sought to counter this ignorance and to widen their horizons. This he did by joining them in intellectual debate about cultivation of their land. He used his scientific knowledge to challenge them and where possible assist and educate them within their own profession. In this realm of scientific education he was more widely successful with the group. Even some of the most distrustful of East Anglian farmers were reached by his relentless efforts to engage them in a scientific approach to agriculture—to convert them from "the art of husbandry" to the "science of agriculture".

The Hadleigh Farmers' Club (Hadleigh was the post town six miles from Hitcham) met monthly and Henslow attended when he could, joining in discussions and giving occasional lectures on scientific aspects of agriculture. It was on the occasion of the anniversary of the club on 16th December, 1842, that he was asked to give a lecture which led to valuable and continued dialogues between himself and the East Anglian farmers. Henslow, seeing the invitation as an opportunity to propound scientific methods in farming, naturally accepted the challenge. His address made an impact not only in East Anglia but beyond. The particular lecture was on the "fermentation of manures" a subject that had arisen in discussions at Hadleigh on a previous occasion. The address was received well[2] and was followed up by no fewer than fifteen instructive letters by Henslow in the *Bury and Norwich Post* over the period 7th January to 20th April 1843 and later collected together in one volume.[3]

These letters were, in fact, an open invitation to farmers to engage in scientific experiment in the field of agriculture. In the first of the series he asserted "we must have more out of the land than our fathers had". He claimed that English education—including that of Cambridge and

Oxford—did not enable men to appreciate the value of scientific enquiry. He chided the farmers that there may be much talk about science, for example, agricultural chemistry, but that this is frequently not understood. There was a tendency, he claimed, to rush in without proper trials. He thus exhorted the farmers, "You must experiment for yourselves". An experiment for testing the value of Liebig's work was then outlined.[4] "Should gypsum be added to manure heaps to fix the ammonia?" was the question to be answered.

The scientific approach was clearly defined and farmers of Suffolk were invited by Henslow to engage in the work as proposed.

"The mode of trying the experiment should be as follows: two dunghills are to be prepared as nearly alike in all respects as possible to make them; one with and the other without, the addition of gypsum. Two separate and equal portions of the same field are to be manured with these. I shall say nothing about the respective quantities of the materials, or the time they are to be allowed to rot. A little variety among the numerous trials I expect to hear of, will be useful, and indeed necessary, to the speedy determination of the important problem to be solved. Let the gypsum be sifted over the several layers as they are deposited in one of the heaps. I would suggest there should be about enough to just cover the surface, without placing it on very thick. The return should give precise information of the following particulars; and any others that may suggest themselves."

The nature of the return which the farmers were requested to send to Henslow is indicated by the following list of items:—

1. The quantity of straw used in each heap.
2. The quantity of animal excreta.
3. On what day each begun.
4. On what day each completed.
5. On what day they were carried and deposited on the soil.
6. The number of loads and weight of each.
7. The extent of land manured by each.
8. The quantity of gypsum used to one of the dung-hills.
   Note carefully—a comparatively small quantity is all that can be required.
9. Any difference in the coming up and appearance of the crops on each piece of land.
10. When each arrive at maturity.
11. The *precise* amount of the produce.
    N.B. It is needless to reply to this question by guess or estimate. It must be answered by scales.
12. Any peculiarity in the quality of each produce.

Thus we see a straightforward attempt to interest the farmers of the area in the scientific method of enquiry into a problem directly related to their own interests. It certainly stimulated both comment and action amongst the farming community. One particular response is singled out for comment because of its later influence on Henslow's work in the area. Bree of Ipswich criticised the experiment on scientific grounds and in scientific terms in the same columns of the *Bury and Norwich Post*.[5] He justly pointed to the limitations of Henslow's experimental design. For example, Bree expressed doubts as to there being adequate moisture for the gypsum to be effective. Much more important, was his suggestion of a control situation for the experiment. He rightly indicated that a third experimental plot treated with gypsum alone was necessary for the proper performance of the experiment. A lively scientific exchange between Henslow and Bree ensued in which Henslow referred to Dr Daubney's work in Oxford and justified the omission of the third plot in local experiments in the interest of simplicity.[6] In late February, Henslow and Bree decided to get together and try out the experiment. Mutual respect and a lasting friendship developed out of this controversy and Henslow subsequently received endless support from Bree in his educational work in the parish and at Ipswich Museum. He gained Bree's genuine admiration both for his scientific ability and his educational endeavours and we have already seen how ready Bree was to support Henslow in his work with the labouring classes of Hitcham.

Henslow's lively scientific approach was, of course, met with less helpful reactions from other farmers. Some of their criticisms enraged the rector. In March he tilted at the pessimists,[7]

> "I do not know why it is that I cannot proceed a step in these endeavours to point out to you the necessity of experimental co-operation for the advancement of agriculture without being met (I won't say obstructed) by sundry hints and surmises that my task is a hopeless one."

The professor had circulated skeleton schedules throughout the county for the entry of individual results. Sceptical comments such as "never yet knew a farmer who could correctly fill up a schedule of any sort" did not deter Henslow. There were evidently substantial and aggravating complaints about the difficulty of filling up these returns. There were angry letters too from farmers demanding time and proper facilities—common enough reactions for men required to engage in new ventures. The man of science was most angered by those farmers who had dared to suggest that it would create such a "bad effect" if the experiment should "fail". These were the cruellest critics of all and their unscientific attitude not unnaturally provoked sharp retort from Henslow who explained with clarity and emphasis that no scientific experiment can fail.[8]

> "Let me see what the results may be, and then let us speculate upon what that result may teach us. With this determination, the experiment cannot fail. It must teach us something. And so of every experiment conducted on correct principles—it never fails. However

it may fail to produce that particular effect which the experimenter may desire, or fancy he can secure, yet even if he should be completely baulked in his expectations, the experiment has assisted him in discovering *the truth*."

So incensed was Henslow at the misunderstanding of scientific method that he proceeded to quote at length an extract from Sir John Henschel's *Discourse on Natural Philosophy*[9] explaining the importance of appeal to facts and the virtue of deductive method.

In spite of criticism, misunderstandings and delays, the experiment proceeded and Henslow referred to farmers "having accepted my challenge (and that in greater numbers than I had called for)". He had hoped for fifty participants and sixty-five had been forthcoming.[10]

Nor were the gypsum experiments the only ones proferred to the farmers of the area. Calling on Sachs' work on photosynthesis, Henslow had referred to the food-producing nature of leaves at a meeting of the Hadleigh Farmers' Club. This had led to one of the members devising his own experiment. A farmer, Mr Rand, of Hadleigh, writes in the *Bury Post*, 19th April, of a three-plot experiment to discover the effect of stripping leaves of mangel-wurzels.[11] He claimed to have been inspired to undertake this experiment as a result of a chance remark of Henslow at the Hadleigh Club. This idea of Henslow's had, in fact, been followed up by him in Letter VI "To the Farmers of Suffolk" published in the *Bury Post* in February, 1843.

This remarkable series of letters "To the Farmers of Suffolk" terminated at the end of April when Henslow left Hitcham for Cambridge and his teaching term. The letters appeared in the press alongside those calling for the repeal of the Corn Laws. Henslow saw that a more lasting answer to Britain's grain supply was crop improvement by scientific farming. He thus exhorted "people of good education throughout the country", in Letter XV—26th April, 1843,

"that they should all bestir themselves, each in his own circle, in order to induce the farmers to try whether they cannot better their condition by better husbandry, rather than by waiting helplessly upon Parliament."

The series ended thus with Henslow knowing that he had provoked scientific thought amongst certain farmers and gentry of East Anglia and had introduced them to some of the current findings of science and their clear application to agricultural practice. It does not seem beyond reasonable speculation to suppose that he might also have won from some farmers their potential, if reluctant, support for future educational plans for labourers who worked their land.

* * *

Hadleigh Farmers' Club was a most valuable forum in which Henslow could convey and discuss his scientific ideas. He was sincerely anxious that the farmers should more fully understand the scientific principles behind good cultivation and responded sensitively to their problems when misfortunes hit their crops.[12] In 1841, he investigated the diseases then attacking wheat in the area. His findings were published as a scientific yet understandable account in the *Journal of the Royal Agricultural Society* of that year. Berkeley, the famous mycologist, praised Henslow's meticulous observations of the wheat fungus. Henslow had seen differing types of spores arising from the same fungus and this was a real advance in scientific knowledge. Unfortunately, he had not taken sufficient heed of the observations of his local farmers who claimed that "piperage" or barberry bushes "blighted the wheat"! Later work proved the validity of the farmers' hunch. A stage of Uredo (the wheat fungus) was found on barberry leaves and this discovery led ultimately to a measure of disease control.

When the red clover crop failed locally in 1844, Henslow investigated the crops concerned. He suggested possible physiological causes in a *Gardener's Chronicle* article which initiated a useful correspondence on that subject. Further, the failure of the potato crop throughout Britain in 1845, was not unnaturally the main topic of discussion at the Hadleigh Farmers' Club meeting in September of that year. Henslow interested himself deeply in the disaster and, in addition to describing the nature of the blight, he gave practical advice on methods of salvaging the starch from the blighted tubers lying in the local farmland.

Henslow's concern for scientific advance in agriculture was ever with him and his tutored eye led to the important finding of valuable beds of phosphate nodules while he was on his family holiday in Felixstowe in 1843.[13] Some of the newly discovered material, locally called coprolites, was sent to the experimental station at Rothamstead while further amounts were distributed to farmers and quickly used locally in Suffolk and Cambridgeshire to manure the soil. The professor noted a high percentage of phosphate of lime in the nodules (56%), saw their potential as fertilisers and wrote of his discovery in the *Gardener's Chronicle* in 1844. It is interesting to note that two enterprising young men left the land from north-east Suffolk to make their fortune from the professor's discovery! This story is legend and is retold by Allan Jobson describing village life in north-east Suffolk in his book *An House Glass on the Run* published in London in 1959. He describes the fate of the nodules based on his grandparents' memory of that time.

> "Coprolites were another dressing discovered about this time. This fossilised excrement of ancient animals had been discovered near the coastal regions of the Red Cragg, and women and children were set to picking these stone-like objects from the fields. Coprolites were also raised from pits, and washed, then taken to a mill and crushed. One of the Dasham mills was used for this purpose. They were also

shipped to London and used at the experimental station at Rothamstead, having been discovered by a Suffolk parson, the Rev. Professor J. S. Henslow, whilst on holiday at Felixstowe in 1843, in the cragg cliff there.

Both grandparents had cause to remember this peculiar and most effective dressing, for grandmother's brothers, two young men, pulled up their roots and migrated to King's Lynn, a thing unheard of, and literally made their fortunes in artificial manures."

Henslow's close and continuous contact with the farming community and their problems enabled him to encourage scientific agricultural practice in the locality. Characteristically, he worked hard to maintain his links with these farming men. Although many opposed him strongly in his role as a parish priest, yet they respected him as a scientist interested in their land. They continued to ask him to speak to them on a variety of scientific topics, some outside their immediate parochial concerns. A letter from Henslow[14] to Thomas Martin on 29th February 1848, indicates that he was currently preparing a lecture for them on the "Geographical Distribution of Alimentary Plants". Another letter[15] on 22nd September 1849, although it inveighs against the ignorance of the farmers and their attitudes to the benefit clubs, conveys the information that Henslow is nevertheless gathering fossils to illustrate a lecture to those same farmers at Hadleigh on the "Tertiary Strata". Furthermore, he gave priority to such local invitations above all else. Writing to Bree[16] on Christmas Day, 1851, he told him that he was working against the clock but he felt obliged to fulfil a Hadleigh commitment.

". . . I am going to give an opening lecture at the Town Hall at Hadleigh in about a fortnight—I could not well refuse my own post-town, or I should have said—nothing for three months may tempt me from home—"

Henslow went on to seek assistance from his scientific friend by asking Bree, "Where are Liebig's new views on Diastase to be found?" The inhabitants of Hadleigh and the surrounding countryside were to receive some recent scientific information, it would seem.

Henslow's educational and scientific work with the farmers of Suffolk was doubtless as stimulating for him as it was for them. It was certainly within the spirit of the scientific age, but a remarkable involvement for a country rector. There is no doubt that he gained the farmers' respect. Local memory testifies in praise of his efforts. His acceptance as a man of agriculture was expressed cogently by an octogenarian, living on the family farm in Hitcham in 1963, who asserted,

"They don't have parsons like that nowadays. They are all academic. Henslow was interested in the land."

(xxii)   Two views of Henslow's Walk, Botanical Gardens, Cambridge.

RULES

FOR THE

BOTANIC GARDEN

Made by the Governors, Oct. 28, 1854.

The BOTANIC GARDEN is open, during daily hours, appointed by the Governors, to

All Graduates of the University.

All Undergraduates, giving their Name and College, if required.

All respectably dressed Strangers, on condition of giving their Name and Address, if required.

Servants with Children, and Children by themselves, are not to be admitted; nor parties with dogs.

The Hot-houses may be visited from ONE to FOUR o'Clock, by persons accompanied by the Curator.

(xxiv) Coprolites.

Ipswich Museum

(xxv) The educational collections in the South Kensington Museum.

(xxvi)   Ipswich Museum—sketch of frontage of new museum building.

Ipswich Record Office

(xxvii)   Membership ticket for Ipswich Museum.

Ipswich Record Office

PORTRAITS

OF

HONORARY MEMBERS OF THE IPSWICH MUSEUM.

PUBLISHED

By GEORGE RANSOME, F.L.S., ETC., HON. SEC.

Dedicated, with Permission, to Her Majesty the Queen and H.R.H. Prince Albert.

HIS ROYAL HIGHNESS PRINCE ALBERT, K.G., F.R.S., PATRON of the IPSWICH MUSEUM.

GEORGE BIDDELL AIRY, M.A., D.C.L., F.R.S., Astronomer Royal.

GEORGE ALLMAN, M.D., F.R.C.S.I., M.R.I.A., etc., Professor of Botany in the University of Dublin, Examiner in Zoology and Botany in the Queen's University in Ireland, Author of 'Biological Contributions,' 'Report on Fresh-water Polyzoa,' etc.

DAVID THOMAS ANSTED, F.R.S. and G.S., Professor of Geology in King's College, Author of 'The Ancient World,' 'Elementary Course of Geology,' etc.

ROBERT BALL, LL.D., F.R.I.A., Sec. R.Z.S., Director of the Dublin University Museum, Secretary to the Queen's University in Ireland, Author of Papers on the Phocidæ, Cephalopoda, Fossil Oxen and Fossil Bears found in Ireland.

SIR HENRY T. DE LA BECHE, C.B., F.R.S., F.G.S., etc., Director-General of the Geological Survey of the United Kingdom, Author of 'Researches in Theoretical Geology,' 'The Geological Observer,' etc.

THOMAS BELL, Sec. R.S., Professor of Zoology in King's College, VICE-PRESIDENT of the IPSWICH MUSEUM, Author of 'History of British Reptiles,' 'British Crustacea,' etc.

SIR JOHN P. BOILEAU, BART., F.R.S., VICE-PRESIDENT of the IPSWICH MUSEUM.

CHARLES LUCIEN BONAPARTE, PRINCE of CANINO, Author of 'Fauna Italica,' 'Continuation of Wilson's Ornithology,' etc.

JAMES SCOTT BOWERBANK, F.R.S., L.S., and G.S., Author of 'Fossil Fruits and Seeds,' etc.

THE MOST NOBLE THE MARQUIS OF BRISTOL, F.R.S., PATRON of the IPSWICH MUSEUM.

ROBERT BROWN, D.C.L., F.R.S., Pres. L.S., etc., Author of 'Prodromus Floræ Novæ Hollandiæ,' etc.

VERY REV. WILLIAM BUCKLAND, D.D., F.R.S., L.S., and G.S., Corr. Mem. Inst. Fr., and VICE-PRESIDENT of the IPSWICH MUSEUM, Professor of Geology, Oxford, Dean of Westminster, Author of 'Reliquiæ Diluvianæ,' 'Bridgewater Treatise,' etc. (From a daguerreotype by Claudet.)

WILLIAM CARPENTER, M.D., F.R.S. and G.S., Author of 'Animal Physiology,' 'Report on the Microscopic Structure of Shells,' etc.

SIR WILLIAM CUBITT, F.R.S., M.R.I.A., F.R.A.S., etc., President of the Institution of Civil Engineers.

JOHN CURTIS, F.L.S., Author of 'British Entomology.'

EDWARD DOUBLEDAY, F.L.S., Author of 'The Genera of Lepidoptera.'

CHARLES DARWIN, M.A., F.R.S. and G.S., Author of 'Journal of a Naturalist,' etc.

MICHAEL FARADAY, D.C.L., F.R.S., Fullerian Professor of Chemistry in the Royal Institution of Great Britain, Author of 'Chemical Manipulation,' and numerous Papers in the Philosophical Transactions.

EDWARD FORBES, F.R.S. and G.S., Professor of Botany in King's College, VICE-PRESIDENT of the IPSWICH MUSEUM, Author of 'History of British Star-fishes,' 'Essay on the Origin of the British Fauna and Flora,' etc.

EDWARD FORSTER, F.R.S., V.P.L.S., Author of Papers on British Botany.

JOHN GOULD, F.R.S. and L.S., Author of 'Birds of Europe,' 'Birds of Australia,' etc.

ROBERT EDMOND GRANT, M.D., F.R.S., Professor of Comparative Anatomy and Zoology in University College, Author of 'Outlines of Comparative Anatomy,' etc.

JOHN EDWARD GRAY, F.R.S. and G.S., Keeper of the Zoological Department of the British Museum, Author of numerous Zoological Papers.

WILLIAM HENRY HARVEY, M.D., Professor of Botany to the Dublin Society, Author of 'History of British Sea-weeds,' 'The Sea-side Book,' etc.

REV. J. S. HENSLOW, M.A., F.L.S. and G.S., Professor of Botany, Cambridge, PRESIDENT of the IPSWICH MUSEUM, Author of 'Principles of Descriptive and Physiological Botany,' etc.

REV. DR. HINDS, BISHOP OF NORWICH, PATRON of the IPSWICH MUSEUM.

SIR WILLIAM JACKSON HOOKER, D.C.L., F.R.S., L.S., and G.S., Director of the Royal Gardens of Kew, Author of 'The British Flora,' 'Curtis's Botanical Magazine,' etc.

JOSEPH DALTON HOOKER, M.D., F.R.S., L.S., and G.S., Author of 'The Botany of the Antarctic Voyage.'

SIR WILLIAM JARDINE, BART., F.R.S.E. and L.S., etc., VICE-PRESIDENT of the IPSWICH MUSEUM, Author of 'The Naturalist's Library,' 'Contributions to Ornithology,' etc.

REV. WILLIAM KIRBY, M.A., F.R.S., L.S., and G.S., late PRESIDENT of the IPSWICH MUSEUM, Author of 'An Introduction to Entomology,' 'Bridgewater Treatise,' etc.

GENERAL SIR EDWARD KERRISON, BART., K.C.B., HON. MEM. IPSWICH MUSEUM.

EDWIN LANKESTER, M.D., F.R.S. and L.S., V.P. London Med. Soc., Professor of Natural History in New College, London, and Translator of Schleiden's 'Principles of Scientific Botany.'

JOHN LEE, LL.D., F.R.A.S., Author of 'Antiquarian Researches in the Ionian Islands,' and Founder of the Hartwell Observatory.

JOHN LINDLEY, Phil. D., F.R.S. and L.S., Professor of Botany, Univ. Coll., London, Author of 'The Vegetable Kingdom,' 'School Botany,' etc.

SIR CHARLES LYELL, M.A., F.R.S. and L.S., President of the Geological Society, VICE-PRESIDENT of the IPSWICH MUSEUM, Author of 'Principles of Geology,' 'Travels in North America,' etc.

DAVID WILLIAM MITCHELL, B.A., F.L.S., Secretary of the Zoological Society of London, Illustrator of 'The Genera of Birds.'

SIR RODERICK IMPEY MURCHISON, M.A., F.R.S. and L.S., V.P.G.S., Hon. Mem. R.S. Ed. and R.I.A., M. Imp. Ac. Sc. St. Petersb., Corr. Mem. Inst. Fr., R. Ac. Ber., Tur., etc., Author of 'The Silurian System,' 'The Geology of Russia and the Ural Mountains, Alps, Apennines, and Carpathians,' etc.

RICHARD OWEN, V.P.R.S., F.G.S., etc., Hunterian Professor of Comparative Anatomy in the College of Surgeons, VICE-PRESIDENT of the IPSWICH MUSEUM, Author of 'History of British Fossil Mammals and Birds,' 'Memoir of the Pearly Nautilus,' etc.

ROBERT PATTERSON, V.P. Nat. Hist. and Phil. Soc. Belfast, Author of 'Zoology for Schools,' etc.

JOHN PHILLIPS, F.R.S. and G.S., Professor of Geology, Author of 'Geology of the Mountain Limestone,' 'Geology of the Yorkshire Coast,' etc.

LYON PLAYFAIR, C.B., F.R.S., etc., Chemist to the Museum of Practical Geology, Author of 'Report on the State of Large Towns in the Manufacturing Districts,' and various Chemical Memoirs.

JAMES RANSOME, HON. MEM. IPSWICH MUSEUM.

LOVELL REEVE, F.L.S., Corr. Mem. Nat. Hist. Soc. Wirtemberg and New York, Author of 'Conchologia Systematica,' 'Conchologia Iconica,' 'Geographical Distribution of Land Mollusca,' etc.

REV. STEPHEN J. RIGAUD, M.A., F.R.A.S., Editor of 'Correspondence of Newton and his Contemporaries.'

RIGHT HON. LORD RENDLESHAM, M.P., VICE-PRESIDENT of the IPSWICH MUSEUM.

SIR JAMES CLARKE ROSS, Capt. R.N., D.C.L., F.R.S. and L.S., Author of 'Voyage to the Southern Seas,' etc.

LIEUTENANT-COLONEL EDWARD SABINE, V.P.R.S., F.R.A.S., Corr. Mem. Imp. Acad. St. Petersburg, etc.

REV. ADAM SEDGWICK, F.R.S. and G.S., Woodwardian Professor of Geology in the University of Cambridge, VICE-PRESIDENT of the IPSWICH MUSEUM, Author of 'A Discourse on the Studies of the University of Cambridge,' 'Remarks on the Structure of Large Mineral Masses,' etc.

PRIDEAUX JOHN SELBY, F.L.S. and G.S., M.W.S., Author of 'British Ornithology,' 'British Forest Trees,' etc.

REV. EDWIN SIDNEY, M.A., VICE-PRESIDENT of the IPSWICH MUSEUM, Author of 'Blights of the Wheat and their Remedies,' 'Electricity, its Phenomena, Laws,' etc.

WILLIAM SPENCE, F.R.S. and L.S., V.P. Ent. Soc., VICE-PRESIDENT of the IPSWICH MUSEUM, Author of 'An Introduction to Entomology,' etc.

REV. DR. STANLEY, F.R.S., Pres. L.S., late BISHOP OF NORWICH, and PATRON of the IPSWICH MUSEUM.

RICHARD TAYLOR, Under Secretary L.S., F.R.A.S., F.S.A., Mem. Nat. Hist. Soc. Mosc., Author of Notes and Additions to Tooke's 'Diversions of Purley' and to Warton's 'History of English Poetry.'

WILLIAM THOMPSON, President Nat. Hist. and Phil. Soc. Belfast, Author of 'The Birds of Ireland,' etc.

NATHANIEL WALLICH, M.D., F.R.S.L. and E., F.L.S. and G.S., Author of 'Plantæ Asiaticæ Rariores,' etc.

GEORGE R. WATERHOUSE, V.P. Entomological Society, Author of 'History of the Mammalia,' etc.

JOHN O. WESTWOOD, F.L.S., Pres. Ent. Soc.; Corr. Mem. Nat. Hist. Soc. Mosc., Lund., Boston, U.S., etc.; Author of 'An Introduction to the Modern Classification of Insects,' 'Arcana Entomologica,' etc.

WILLIAM YARRELL, V.P.L.S. and Z.S., VICE-PRESIDENT of the IPSWICH MUSEUM, Author of 'History of British Birds,' 'History of British Fishes,' etc.

T. B. WESTERN, Esq., VICE-PRESIDENT of the IPSWICH MUSEUM.

IPSWICH,
1852.

(xxix) Museum, Kew—The Economic botany room was arranged by Henslow.
*Crown Copyright, reproduced with the permission of the Controller of Her
Majesty's Stationery Office, and of the Director, Royal Botanic Gardens, Kew*

Department of Science and Art,
South Kensington, London, S.W.

15 day of July 1857

My dear Professor

In wishing you to shut the Paris Case in order we have always contemplated the payment of all Expenses connected with it and also in connection with the Inspection of a ty special Series of Plants for the Educational Museum. Far from Considering you in any way unreasonable

(xxx)   Recompense for work for Paris Exhibition—Lyon Playfair to Henslow, 1857.
Extract of letter from Library, Kew Gardens

(xxxi)   The Royal Children.   *Illustrated London News*

(xxxii)   Botany lessons for the Royal Children—an extract from Clark's letter, 1850,
inviting Henslow to the Palace.   *The Library, Kew Gardens*

CHAPTER EIGHT

Museums for the People

THE town of Ipswich lies in the south east of Suffolk, 14 miles from Hitcham village. In 1847, a group of interested individuals (Henslow included) established a museum in the town as part of a system for giving "Instruction to the Working Classes in Ipswich in various branches of Science and more especially in Natural History".[1] Several small collections in the town were put together to form the nucleus of the museum. One of these important local collections was contributed by an old Cambridge acquaintance of Henslow's, the entomologist Rev. W. Kirby of Barham, Suffolk, who became the new museum's first President.

The task of developing the museum as a successful educational institution called for expertise in natural history and an enthusiasm for popular education. It seemed inevitable that Professor Henslow should become deeply involved in the work and, at the first meeting of subscribers, he was indeed elected vice-president and succeeded as president only two years later when Kirby died. From that moment onward Henslow actively guided the development of the museum, giving generously of his time, skill and materials until the end of his life.

Certainly, no man could have been better able to influence the work of the institution than Henslow for he enjoyed hugely both the collection and organisation of museum materials. He was convinced that only by careful selection, systematic arrangement and adequate labelling of materials could they be of any real educational benefit to the public. He had a lifetime of experience to call on and an undying enthusiasm for museum work and popular scientific education.

Even while a young boy, Henslow had been surrounded by natural history materials in his father's home and frequently collected specimens from the banks of the Medway where he played. When he moved from his Rochester mathematical school to Dr Jephson's school in Camberwell, he had the good fortune to receive special instruction in zoology from Dr Leach, an accepted expert in crustacea and responsible for much of the cataloguing of zoological material at the British Museum at that time. The boy Henslow was able to assist a little in this responsible task.[2]

His skill in museum work was quickly spotted a few years later by Adam Sedgwick, Professor of Geology at Cambridge, who saw that the young Henslow's assistance would be invaluable in collecting and arranging the mineral exhibits in the university's Woodwardian Museum. Thus, as a young Fellow of St John's College in 1820, Henslow's help was enlisted and he was sent straightaway to seek out and negotiate for a prehistoric elk known to have been found on the Isle of Man the previous year. He landed in Ramsay Bay after a stormy, thirty hour passage from Liverpool. With characteristic energy he set forth on his quest the following day "having borrowed a horse of one man and a saddle of another" and tracked down the elk (reconstructed by a blacksmith) in a caravan at Bishop's Court where it was being exhibited as a curiosity.[3]

The Woodwardian Audit[4] of the following year told nothing of this achievement but noted due recognition of "the assistance of Mr. Henslow in arranging the minerals". The arrangement of a series of English strata, commencing with the granite of Cornwall, and ending with the alluvial deposits of Suffolk is of particular interest because it certainly influenced his future museum work in the field of mineralogy. The exhibition of minerals according to the geological time-scale was adopted for the Ipswich Museum later and has been retained there to this day.

The Woodwardian Audit for 1822 recorded yet more activity in that museum and spelled out Henslow's typical generosity as well as his conscientiousness and drive. The audit noted gratefully,

> "The Museum has also received a very valuable accession in a collection presented by Mr. Henslow, which consists of over a hundred specimens carefully selected during a geological survey of the Isle of Anglesea and illustrated by a memoir—and sections which will be published in the next number of the Cambridge Transactions. Mr. Henslow has undertaken the arrangement of this collection which occupies 24 drawers."

Nor had this young Fellow yet completed his task for the Woodwardian Museum. He spent the following Christmas vacation arranging a further collection of minerals with Sedgwick who worked with him until mid-January when the Professor of Geology was called away due to a family bereavement.

Henslow's earlier natural history interests had actually been in zoology and in some measure he made good the lack of studies in that subject at Cambridge—there was no Chair in Zoology—by building up a Zoological Museum there. In a *Memoir* to him,[5] 1861, The Cambridge Philosophical Society admitted freely that,

> "It was Henslow's patient devotion to zoology which enabled him to form an excellent Museum, long the only zoological Museum in the University, and the legitimate parent of that larger family of museums which have grown up and are still growing up in the Botanic Garden."

Of the natural history sciences, Henslow perhaps knew least of botany when he took his Regius Chair in the subject in 1827. With characteristic zeal he set about mastering the subject and certainly some of his knowledge was acquired while developing the botanical museum there. A jumble of deteriorating plant specimens confronted him when he took over the department. Immediately, with characteristic energy and determination, he set to work sorting through them, preserving the best and arranging them in a systematic way. To this rescued nucleus he added a fine collection of British plants built up largely by his own efforts.[6]

The Department also received valuable donations from Cambridge graduates and others returning from journeys of exploration or periods of service overseas. These, too, were carefully organised and preserved. Henslow's enthusiasm grew, his expertise was highly respected and he persuaded the university to acquire some very valuable collections for the botanical museum. Not least among these was the collection of 30,000 plants collected in Mauritius and Gibraltar by C. M. Lemann, M.D.(Cantab.). Joseph Hooker,[7] wrote to George Bentham (the botanist who had arranged the Lemann herbarium), of Henslow's successful negotiations,

> "Henslow scouting the idea of valuing species or specimens because they were unique has told well, and proved to the Dons that such collections have other and higher value than old china."

Joseph Hooker had good reason to know and admire Professor Henslow's knowledge and ability in botany and also his extraordinary skills in museum work. Joseph's father, Sir William, had persuaded Henslow to help him with the museum and herbarium at Kew when these gardens were given to the nation. Sir William was appointed to develop the museum and Henslow was asked by him to collect and organise the section on economic botany. Henslow's biographer, Jenyns, writes of the generosity and practical manual skills Henslow brought to that task.

> "Not only did he contribute largely to its stores, by a free remittance of the best and finest specimens he could supply of whatever came into his possession deserving a place among its collections, but he assisted both in the general arrangement of the whole, and in details connected with the operations of cutting, mounting and ticketing the specimens, so as to adapt them best for public exhibition."

Sir William was grateful to the professor for his industry and enterprise and wrote simply from his sick-bed, some time in 1845,[8]

> "I write from bed and cannot add more except to thank you for all you are kindly doing for our museum."

Today, a marble bust of Professor Henslow stands at Kew in tribute to his valued part in developing the national museum there.

*   *   *

Of a very different and strictly temporary nature were the fascinating marquee museums set up by the professor on Hitcham's rectory lawn every summer and autumn as a regular feature of the village horticultural shows. These exhibitions were tended with the same conscientious care as Henslow's other more sophisticated museums and their great success in communicating with the village labourers was due overwhelmingly to his careful selection of exhibits to relate closely to the visitors' interests. (Among items chosen were British mammals, rice in the ear, pearls from British molluscs, ostrich eggs, tobacco plant.) He insisted also on the attractive presentation of new material. His brother-in-law described how the dimensions of the trunk of the great mammoth tree (Wellingtonia) were, for example, traced on the rectory lawn alongside a diagram showing its size, relative to other known British trees.

An important device for interesting and educating the visitors to the marquee museum was Henslow's use of lecturets which he would deliver to the parishioners as they were gathered about the exhibits. He quickly realised that a number of short talks was greatly preferable to one long one for the purpose, as he confessed in a letter to his friend Thomas Martin in October 1853. Experience had indeed taught him to have regard for the limits of his audience's span of attention.[9]

A wide variety of the specimens and materials from which Henslow selected his marquee exhibits were stored in the rectory itself and, before that in his Cambridge home. His friends were happy to augment the collection or to loan materials when needed as they knew the excellent use made of them. Darwin, who had been a frequent and welcome guest at the Henslow home, was familiar with the intriguing collection and wrote from the *Beagle*[10] in 1842 that new treasures are on their way to the rectory.

"September 18 (1842)

My dear Henslow,

I bequest your Museum a Parcel of Paints with which Fuegians colour their bodies. Two spears with which they spear Porpoises, Fish, Otters and Guaraco etc.—And a Pacific Dophin's Hook.

Ever yours,
C. DARWIN."

Assistance of various kinds was forthcoming also from Henslow's colleague Sir William Hooker at Kew. Extracts from two of his letters[11] show the sympathy with which he responded to the professor's requests and the good humour with which he attended to them.

"August 17, 1850

. . . You can have another long bamboo cane and welcome and one for Ipswich. We shall be felling soon. You shall have a Cane of Wellingtonia and a piece of wood of Wellingtonia if you do not keep them long . . . W.H."

"September 6 [no year]

. . . I am going to the Museum as soon as breakfast of over to compare your list and if I see any objects which I think worth sending, I will insert [?] a note of them and you can have the loan of them if worth the sending . . . W.H."

Henslow's wide and varied experience of museum work and his zeal in collecting and cataloguing had awakened rather than dulled his awareness of the educational potential of these institutions. By the time Professor Henslow became closely involved with Ipswich Museum, his contact with museums at national and parish level had given him unique insight. He was not only familiar with the techniques of displaying materials but was aware of the impact made by exhibits on ordinary men and women. Any natural history museum would be of little value, he believed, if it were not visited and enjoyed by the public themselves.

* * *

Henslow's first major task for the Ipswich Museum was to deliver the introductory lecture in 1848 and to convince the leading citizens of Ipswich of the value of the natural sciences in general and of natural history in particular. The address was a masterly and human presentation of his own philosophical stand as a scientist. He extolled the usefulness of science as a body of knowledge which dispelled fear, myth and ignorance; characteristically, too, he justified its study as a mental discipline which he found too often lacking even in learned men of the day;[12] and finally he countered any notion of the supposed interference of science with the proper understanding of religion.

But it was not until his election, two years later, as president of the museum after Kirby's death that Henslow's practical and scientific influence was fully exerted. The occasion of his installation as President perhaps mapped the way that future developments were to take.[13] Professor E. Forbes (Professor of Botany at Kings College, London), an eminent geologist, was invited to honour the occasion and "went down to Ipswich to give a gratis lecture, for the benefit of the Museum there, on its anniversary meeting". In his address he outlined his views on provincial museums which accorded closely with Henslow's own. They formed the basis on which work proceeded in the following decade. Forbes regretted that museums of that day were,

"—too often ambitious attempts at general collections, and, necessarily, failures. Too many of them are little better than curiosity shops. In their best aspect they are, with very few exceptions more costly and far less useful than they ought to be."

He outlined his ideal provincial Natural History Museum which he felt should consist of three departments, for which three spacious rooms, if properly constructed, would suffice—

1. *A Local Collection*, illustrative of the Zoology, Botany and Geology of the county or district.
2. *A Teaching Collection*, consisting of carefully selected, well-arranged and thoroughly labelled types of the classes, Orders, Families and teaching genera of Animals and Plants of the series of geological formations and their characteristic fossils, and of Minerals—no superfluous specimens to be admitted.
3. *A Miscellaneous Collection*, including fine or rare specimens of exotic productions not necessary for the teaching collection, remarkable curiosities, and ethnological illustrations.

A distinguished gathering heard Forbes' address. Acceptance of natural science in Ipswich seemed assured. In addition to Forbes himself, visitors to Ipswich that night included van Voorst, R. Taylor (naturalist and printer), Bowerbank (geologist and partner in a London distillery), Mitchell (probably the scientific writer), and Lankester (Professor of Natural History, London). George Ransome, the museum committee's "indefatigable secretary",[14] had certainly worked hard to give Henslow a successful start. He entertained these distinguished men at his home together with local dignitaries. Forbes' account reflects the optimism of the evening.

"Henslow had been installed as their new President. I stayed with Ransome, who gave a dinner-party when it was pleasant to see the bishop, four or five clergymen, and a bushel of naturalists, all dining at the table of a quaker chemist and druggist."

The town had noted the importance of the museum venture and its aims, and future structure had now been publicly outlined.

In spite of the euphoria surrounding Henslow's installation, the new president had troubles enough to come. There was little money coming in and the list of subscribers was seriously dwindling through deaths and disinclination to pay. Fortuitously, the British Association selected Ipswich as their venue for the general meeting in 1851, and this, incidentally, injected new life into the museum's fortunes.

Ipswich had been selected by the British Association for its 1851 meeting because it was the town of Messrs Ransome and May who had engineered the supporting structures for the new large lens installed at Greenwich Royal Observatory that very year.[15] The business of the meeting[16] was presided over by the Astronomer Royal and one of the honoured guests was none other than H.R.H. Prince Albert who was escorted round the many exhibits in the town. His visits included one to Ipswich Museum and the occasion is recorded in the *Illustrated London News* for July, 1851.

". . . The Prince was received in the entrance Hall by Professor Henslow, President of the Museum; the Vice-Presidents; and Messrs. F. W. Johnson and G. Ransome, the Secretaries, by whom he was conducted upstairs to the collection room. His Royal Highness was attended by the Marquis of Abercromby, Colonel Grey and Colonel Seymour. His entrance was a signal for a general rising, accompanied by other demonstrations of respect and welcome, which the Prince gracefully acknowledged. Arrived at the chair provided for his accommodation his Royal Highness took up a position on one side of it.

Professor Henslow, the President, then read a congratulatory address; the document having been received by the Prince, and by him placed in the hands of Colonel Grey, his Royal Highness read out a most gracious reply which he afterwards handed to Professor Henslow."

The Prince then studied the exhibits in the Museum and evidently approved the lay out of the materials—

". . . he commenced a regular inspection of the cases of the collection and frequently expressed his gratification on the extent and value of the collection, and with the admirable manner in which it had been arranged."

His Royal Highness and other eminent visitors to Ipswich that summer were certainly made aware of the museum and the hopes for its future. The newly printed list of subscribers to the museum* for the year following the British Association's Ipswich meeting was headed by H.R.H. Prince Albert himself and read more like the roll of the Royal Society than friends of a provincial museum!

Not unnaturally Henslow sought help from these famous subscribers over the years and the minutes of the museum management committee reveal that they and other friends of Henslow frequently and generously contributed towards the expenses of the museum and the acquisition of new exhibits. Unfortunately, George Ransome the secretary was too enthusiastic in his rush for gold, albeit with the museum's benefit as his sole motive. An equivocal response from Prince Albert to Ransome's appeal for funds brought the museum's financial problems to a head and the committee under Henslow investigated the museum's sad financial straits. They discovered the museum to be heavily in debt. The management committee had not been fully informed of the extent. In late summer, 1852, they learned of the true situation and of the attempts made unilaterally by George Ransome to raise money from the subscribers to offset disaster. Henslow chaired the various committee meetings during the crisis and he must have been truly sorry, though obliged, to seek the secretary's resignation[17] in August for misplaced zeal and lack of consultation. At the fifth anniversary meeting in December the situation was publicly revealed in the annual report—[18]

*See Appendix II.

". . . in the early part of July application was made by Mr. George Ransome through Lord Grey to His Royal Highness, Prince Albert for a donation to the funds of the Museum. In reply Lord Grey requested some information as to the state of our funds . . .

. . . on 24th of July 1852, a communication was received from Lord the Honourable L. B. Phipps, Keeper of the Privy Purse, addressed to Mr. George Ransome, from which the following is an extract referring to previous correspondence 'in that letter you state that in order to free the Institution from debt it is necessary to raise the sum of £500. I have received the commands of His Royal Highness to acquaint you that whenever there shall have been collected for this purpose £400 His Royal Highness will contribute the £100 to complete the sum required'."

Some subscriptions had been forthcoming but the debt remained grave.

Professor Henslow seldom abandoned an educational enterprise through lack of money. He sought alternative funding and it was under his chairmanship that the management committee resolved, in November 1852, "that the Museum be offered to the town of Ipswich to be maintained by a borough rate".[19]

The application to the town was successful[20] and the Burgesses decided to use their powers under the Public Libraries and Museums Act of 1850.

"The votes of the Burgesses of the Town were taken on 4th of February, when the members were 709 for the museum and 69 against it, being a majority of 640 or 10 to 1 in favour of its becoming a public institution of the Town."

The Mayor became Chairman of the museum's new management committee and it was not long before Henslow was asked to resume office as the museum's president. On 16th June he accepted the invitation[21] and was so enabled to guide the institution's development once again.

Financial worries were near their end. The current debt was to be discharged and the professor and his friends rallied to this cause.[22]

But financial problems were not the only ones inherited by Henslow on his appointment as President in 1850. He was committed to developing a museum open to the public yet he was forced to investigate thoroughly allegations of grave misconduct by the townsfolk on the "free nights" during which they visited the museum in some numbers. The curator, Dr Clarke, himself a magistrate of the borough, had been so incensed by the disorderly behaviour of the visitors that having frequently and vainly complained to the management committee, he formally wrote at length to Professor Henslow, the president, begging him to talk to this committee and bring about some action in the matter. Clarke's letter and Henslow's considered reply were read to the management committee on 3rd January 1851.[23] Extracts of Clarke's letter revealed the evident distaste with which he viewed free access of the general public to the museum. Yet this free access was fundamental to the purpose of the institution. Clarke complained:

> "I have always been ready to forward the intentions of the subscribers to the Ipswich Museum by affording that aid to the industrious working classes which they have been anxious to obtain but in the prosecution of my duties I have long discovered, to my great mortification, that the meetings at the Museum, intended for the improvement of the people, are on the contrary having a most demoralising result from the indiscriminate nature of the admissions."

He then proceeded to describe "the vile and disorderly mob that contaminates our room on public nights" and referred to their "obscene conversations", and "indelicate and blasphemous retorts to girls who have pulled them by the hair of their heads or scratched them with their nails as they passed along the room". He objected strongly to their appearance and lack of cleanliness.

> "The dress of many are frequently observed to be covered with dirt, mortar, soot and smelling so abominably that respectably dressed people could not approach them; they were evidently vagabonds of the town and neighbourhood, meeting there only to enjoy themselves in their own indecent way, simply because the room is more comfortable than the streets."

The noise these visitors caused is described with passion. He refused to tell Henslow the "epithets used" but wrote of the "howling, shrieking, whistling with fingers in their mouths and rushing up and down stairs". The litter they caused offended him too.

> "On mornings following these events, I have picked up a quantity of orange peel, shells of pinpatches [!] peas, sticks etc. which are usually thrown by these visitors at each other, and at the glass, to make those persons start who are occupied in examining the objects within the cases."

Vandalism was also laid at their door. Visitors were said to have spat at the cases, cut the cloth on the tables, removed parts of the stone exhibits and stolen ornaments from the chandeliers. As for the poor man in the house opposite the museum, Clarke claimed he was in such fear for the safety of his daughter on these dreadful free nights that he was now under medical treatment for the strain! The museum attendant was also said to be suffering from headaches resulting from the strain of the "free nights". Indeed, things it seemed could scarcely be worse. Certainly Clarke claimed "No brothel can be worse"! And all this time the police refused to answer his calls for help.

With calm detachment Henslow investigated each of the allegations in turn and, while accepting a few of them, he found no corroboration for the more extravagant complaints. He replied[24] to Clarke forthrightly,

"I became perfectly satisfied that you had suffered your imagination to get the better of your judgement."

While accepting Clarke's resignation Henslow assured him,

"I shall do my best to assist the committee in putting the Museum into good working conditions and hope soon to meet the working classes and consult with them about the best mode of securing order on free nights."

How consultation was achieved is not recorded. The troubles must have abated for in December 1852, the Annual Report noted that "demonstration and popular instructions have been given to the working classes on the free nights".[25] This measure is reminiscent of Henslow's marquee museums lecturets which proved so intriguing to the villagers of Hitcham. All was not yet solved however, for the committee were forced to the decision in June 1853, of closing the library on "free nights" as it was being used for "improper" purposes. In August of that year more stringent control was placed on entry. The relevant minute is recorded below. The sting is in the tail.

"Ipswich Museum Minutes   4.8.1853.

That all day and evening visitors alike should be requested to write their names individually—or in the case of a party one of that party signing and in the event of a person not being able to write that of a mark or signature of that person appended to the name written for him shall be sufficient provided always that the persons are deemed proper to be admitted by cleanliness and general misdemeanour."

It seems that the trouble ended here and that future order was maintained by the tactful discretion of the museum attendant and good sense of the public at large.

These problems disposed of, the new president could turn his efforts to his main field of influence—the completion of a representative collection of natural history materials and their careful preparation, organisation and exhibition in the museum. It was in this field of activity that his expertise and guidance were anxiously sought.

Materials had been coming in from many quarters. Some were modest: some exotic. The assortment of material is indicated in the selected records reproduced below.

Accessions mentioned in correspondence:

Bird's nest (To Bree of Ipswich to Henslow)[26]

22.7.1851   Thanks for the eggs which are clearly distinct from those in my nest—As you know them to be S. Phray mine must be S. Arundinacra—which is (I believe) the rarer species so much the better for Ipswich Museum.

Fungi (To Henslow from Dr Pereira of Kew)[27]
6.12.1851 I have got a few things for your museum such as stoychnis
    Potatimum and Bassorah galls (supposed to be mala
    sodarutica) but I suppose they must remain until we meet
    as I do not know how to send them to you.

27.12.1851 (To Bree from Henslow)[28]
    In the typical series in Ipswich Museum now in progress
    you will find drawings of mine of Bunt, Smut, Mildew
    appended to the specimens themselves.

Insects (To Bree from Henslow)[29]
30.12.1851 We shall be very glad of Doubleday's assistance in the
    typical series and if he would name such insects as are
    typical of the chief groups of the differents orders it would
    be a great help—Common species if possible.

Accessions recorded in *Ipswich Museum Minutes*

Birds
(1852) Birds from New Zealand.

11.6.1853 Collection of Birds from Falkland Islands were ordered,
    stuffed and set up by Mr Seaman and their eggs placed
    by them.

Skeletons Skeleton of Dog-faced Baboon presented by the Zoo-
(1852) logical Society.

10.5.1852 Skeleton of Boa Constrictor.

Models
10.5.1852 Flowers modelled in wax.

Economic Products of professions of the Honourable East India
15.12.1852 Company. (A selection from specimens shown at Great
    Exhibition.)

Fossils A collection of Fossils of interest and value from D. Saul,
16.6.1853 Esq. 15 Aldersgate St. London.

These and many other materials bid for space in this now struggling museum. Not all the accessions had been properly handled and skins found rotting in the cellar had to be burnt. There was urgent need for a practical man in the day to day supervision of the museum and the arrival of George Knights as curator in November 1853 was providential indeed.

In truth, Henslow, his presidency reaffirmed by the newly-formed management committee, had a hand in Knights' appointment as curator. He had written to the Chairman, Mayor S. H. Cowell, with suggestions for the duties of any incoming curator and the Mayor read these[30] to the next committee who agreed that they should be sent to all aspiring candidates. The crucial prescription for the curator read,

"Without calling upon you to undertake preparing objects (as birds, skins etc.) for the museum, the Curator will expect that the series of specimens arranging under my direction will require some occasional manipulations on your part though no more than I undertake myself, and I shall be happy in instructing you how to complete, and I shall like to know whether you object to work at this sort of manipulation."

No candidate could be in doubt of what was expected of him here and the successful man certainly lived up to Henslow's requirements in this area.

The appointment of curator was critical in other ways too and, while the Mayor administered the exercise, Henslow did all in his power to guide the committee in the appropriate direction. His suggestion that the new curator should also act as museum secretary was accepted and this made for smoother administrative progress of the institution. The need for tolerance and understanding in the curator was essential if the museum was to expand its contact with the people and recover healthy public relations. The professor kept in constant touch with persons more directly involved in the appointment than himself. A letter from his scientific friend Bree[31] helped keep Henslow in the picture up to the time of short listing.

"We have reduced the fifty candidates to three for the curatorship of Ipswich Museum either of whom seems likely to suit us well. I have advised the Mayor to invite these three (paying their expenses) to come and look at the Museum, understand this equals roughly what is expected of them, reply distinctly to a few questions (influenced doubtless by J.S.H.) and then let us decide which is the most likely of the three to suit us best . . ."

From the three interviewees, George Knights was selected and he stayed for twenty years. The professor came to trust and respect him and they became firm friends.[32] Their co-operation and working partnership expedited the scientific and educational progress of the museum and maintained it as a popular educational provision in the town.

Henslow set to work to fill the gaps in the collection at Ipswich and, in June 1853, before Knights' appointment, he had already set a quest in progress for completion of the crag fossil collection[33] (part of the local collection in Forbes' analysis). The appropriate *Minute* reads—

"Attention to a complete collection of Crag Fossils should be one of our primary objects—and as soon as ever there is accommodation secured for such a collection we should be able to get on . . ."

The next committee meeting agreed to the acquisition of glazed drawers for the growing collection of crag from local deposits.

Professor Henslow was especially keen that botanical exhibits should also have a proper place in the new institution. His experience and skill in herbarium work gained in the major collections at Cambridge and Kew was now at the disposal of the less sophisticated—yet to him equally important—project at Ipswich. He sought to persuade the new curator to develop a useful reference collection in botany and to this end he offered his considerable talents. Nor did he lose time in doing so. In February 1854, some of the specimens were evidently ready and he wrote to inform the new curator (using the somewhat formal mode of address—"My dear Sir"—soon to be dropped as the friendship grew).

> "I prepared about half the specimens I brought away, last night—ready for being glued down. I think I shall be able to be in time to be at Rigaud's next lecture and to bring them with me—I have felt no further ill effects from my exertions!"

This injection of practical help and enthusiasm was typical of Henslow's influence on the museum's development. The practical encouragement thus given had obviously borne fruit for a letter to Knights in the autumn shows that progress had been made in the botany section.

> 'I am glad to hear of the plants and will look at them and see how we can continue a consultable Herbarium . . ."

There was no immediate response from Knights but Henslow pursued the matter and ten days later, on 31st October, wrote again politely but firmly to fix a date for consultation,

> "I am anxious to know on what date my services are required at Ipswich—for Mrs. Henslow wants to go over with me. I am always obliged to look out ahead and make my engagements abroad suit with those at home . . ."

A meeting was evidently agreed and he told Knights in a letter of 11th November that he was consulting the highest authorities in the land in preparation for discussions with him about the botany section of Ipswich Museum.

> "I go to Kew on Tuesday to have a talk with Sir William and Dr. Hooker about the requisite types for botany."

A week later he announced his intended visit[34] to Ipswich, presumably to talk over plans with Knights.

And so the botanical work continued to be fostered by Henslow's patient persistence and involvement. As late as 17th February 1857 he corresponded with Knights on the subject of a cabinet to house the herbarium collection. It had obviously reached an acceptable standard now for public access, consultation and exhibition.

Other parts of the museum also received his conscientious attention for he was keen to complete collections on all important sections enumerated by Forbes at the opening ceremony. Even on holiday the work was uppermost in Henslow's mind. On returning from holiday he writes to Knights 2nd October 1854, to say,

"I have picked up some materials for the Museum in my travels. I got back on Saturday night, all the better for my holiday, though the last few days were rather hard work. On Thursday I went down a salt mine at Northwich, got upset in an omnibus and well squeezed in a crowd; back to Warrington to see the Museum . . ."

He could not let opportunities slip by and in the following year, one of stress and overwork for the professor, he set off to Lavenham "to inspect a set of minerals for sale". Later in the autumn he let Knights know that some fossils would be coming from London, "I told Owen",[35] he related, "to send the fossils direct to Ipswich". Whether these were accessioned by the museum is not clear but it seems likely. Certainly a reasonable loan collection had been built up by November of 1856. Some had evidently been mislaid at that time and Henslow enquired anxiously of Knights,

"Did you ever recover the fossil collection from Dr. ? He is a notoriously careless fellow but as honourable as he is scientific."

Henslow was engaged that autumn also in seeking a collection of "Economic Animals". Once again he taps his friends as possible sources of supply. Gray,[36] of the British Museum cannot help but takes the opportunity in his reply to comment sadly upon the disarray amongst scientists in the metropolis.

"British Museum,
27th October 1856.

I am sorry that I don't know where any of the animals you mention are to be procured at a moderate cost . . . I am sorry I cannot help you with any of our specimens but have long thought that a set of Economic Animals that might be loaned would be an advantage but there is so little union among scientific men that it is very difficult to carry out any plan or to act on the Scientific Board."

The archaeological section received attention also and for many years a Roman tessellated pavement stood, according to Henslow's instructions, against the wall of the museum lobby, after the style of such exhibits at the British Museum. It now has pride of place in the museum grounds. The professor was certainly able to judge the value of acquisitions in this section as he had gained a great deal of expertise over the years. Remaining correspondence tells that he had been called to assess archaeological finds near Bury St Edmund's, St Alban's and in Nottinghamshire. It was natural that when Knights had heard of the opportunity to purchase this local antiquity Henslow should have encouraged him to do so if he could find the funds.

". . . Seeing I am always dipping my hand into my pocket on the Museum's account I shan't volunteer a subscription—or if the administration seems overstingy let me know and I will assist. These sort of things are getting rarer and a local antiquity ought to be greedily seized upon."

The deal went through satisfactorily and on 27th August 1857 Henslow rejoiced to Knights,

"I am glad the pavement is in hand—costly as it is, it may be worth preserving."

The professor's collector's eye and master plan certainly facilitated the orderly development of this successful museum. In addition his amazing practical skills were at the disposal of the museum as were the trained resources of the village craftsmen.

Nothing delighted Henslow more than to engage himself in mounting and labelling materials. His collection at Kew had been handled by himself personally. He devised a number of new mounting techniques over the years and these were to be taken up by other museums. His home workshop was the centre of this activity and Jenyns gives a delightful description[37] of Henslow working on a technical problem with his family round about him.—

"He never seemed more thoroughly contented than when at work at his table, on a long winter's evening, with all his specimens and tools about him; now selecting the best specimen of each kind or examining it with a lens; or in some cases paring it with a knife in order to show the interior;—now cutting stiff card-board with strong scissors of a peculiar make he had on purpose;—now moulding soft clay into a suitable form to serve as a stand for specimens that could not otherwise be so well inspected . . .

In such work he would be quite absorbed with his family around him, taking little notice of what others were about. It was always evident that his mind was quite as much engaged as his hands. He would seem to be turning over in his thoughts for what uses each specimen might serve, the impression it each likely to make on the spectator's eye, the instruction it was capable of affording . . ."

A number of the museum's technical problems were solved by "village machinery", as Henslow called the help received from the villagers. His village botanists doubtless helped with herbarium material as they had on previous occasions. His sister, whose illustrative skills assisted the professor many times throughout his career, was recommended as possible adviser when the museum had problems with illustrations and lettering in the early days.[38] The village blacksmith was called in November 1854 to solve a problem after a frustrating episode concerning the manufacture of wire brackets to support museum exhibits. He evidently succeeded in this task. The local machinery was clearly not up to all the carpentry jobs, however, and Henslow apologised to Knights the following year for "the remake of the label stands". "I suppose," he added, "the village carpenter is not up to such a job". He had succeeded in making a successful stand of a head of an Indian elephant, however! Indeed, it could have been the tools that were inadequate for some tasks, for Henslow, four years later, in 1859, had to seek outside help in relation to a wood exhibit. Knights was warned by letter on 19th April,

"I forward by Webb on Thursday 3 logs of wood, which I wish sawed up into specimens in the manner shown in the paper sent—one of each may be retained for the Museum and I want the rest for my private eating.
They are too hard for the village saw . . ."

* * *

Whatever the limitations of the village team there is no doubt that Henslow himself was very competent in the practical and scientific aspects of museum work. This was acknowledged publicly when he was asked by Lyon Playfair, Secretary of the newly formed Department of Science and Art, to send some of his beautifully finished teaching models to the educational section of the Paris Exhibition of 1855. The professor responded enthusiastically and prepared a series of "Carpological Illustrations" representing the structure of fruits. The venture, which was ill-fated in many ways, nevertheless "excited the enthusiasm of the Paris botanists" and was generally approved by the British scientists.

The saga of the Henslow models is worth retelling for it indicates how unused exhibitors were to material of this kind. The story begins with an inappropriate assignment, "Carpological Apparatus", in the Paris catalogue. Henslow wrote to Knights about it on 3rd March 1855.

"In the printed catalogue they have assigned my specimens to a position among surgical instruments under the heading 'Carpological Apparatus'. Dr. Playfair says he will see that this error is corrected, and that they shall be placed among objects intended for educational purposes . . . I am also designated as Professor Henslow of Hadleigh! So easily are blunders committed."

At this point of time the models were in good repair. Henslow added specifically,

"My specimens have travelled so far without a single flowering specimen having become detached and I hope and trust they will get safely to Paris.—I find they have quite satisfied those who have inspected them."

Alas, the exhibits did not stay intact for the June heat of the French capital caused the wax to melt and Knights was thus informed on 18th June,

"I hear my specimens have arrived quite safe at Paris, but that the heat has been so great the wax models have *melted*! To what extent I don't know . . ."

The professor was certainly displeased at this unforeseen catastrophe and Dr Joseph Hooker indicates this when writing about Paris visiting arrangements to Professor John Lindley's son. "I did half promise to go with Henslow" Hooker tells Nathanial Lindley, July 3rd, "but he is disgusted with his wax models having collapsed."[39]

Lyon Playfair of the Department of Science and Art tried to put the matter in perspective in a business letter to the professor[40] on the 11th July by explaining,

"There were a few things detached in transit but Corporal Key was sure he could put them right."

It seems that, models and temper restored, Henslow visited the Paris Exhibition that summer along with other eminent British botanists.

The "carpological" exhibits attracted attention and approval. Henslow not only received a handsome apology and financial compensation for the misfortunes that had befallen his models but commendation, in the form of a medal, for his valued contribution to the education section. Henslow's respected position as scientist and educator emerges clearly from Lyon Playfair's letters to him relating to these matters. The first was written from Cornwall on 12th October 1855.

"I am very sorry indeed to learn that you found your case in such a bad condition. When in Paris I had it handed up but it was not unpacked till the day after I left. It was then reported to be in good condition with the exception of a few detached pieces . . .

Corporal Key took a real interest in the case and I believe acted to the best of his power. Still this does not the less render it unfortunate that such an instructive case as yours should ultimately have become so seriously injured. I enclose Corporal Keys' report.

Personally, I valued your contribution as one of the most important exhibits, and I regret extremely its untoward end—I go to Paris in three days and shall enquire further about it."

The last of Playfair's letters on the subject is dated 15th July 1857 and is written from the Department of Science and Art, South Kensington, offering financial recompense for the work undertaken for the Exhibition.

"In wishing you to put the Paris case in order we have always contemplated the payment of all expenses connected with it and also in connection with the preparation of a typical series of plants for the Educational Museum. Far from considering you in any way unreasonable in these requirements we would gladly pay you a fee for the work rendered in addition to the Expenses because we feel sure that it would be properly bestowed and ultimately find its way for some very useful purpose in the advancement of Education . . ."

Professor Henslow had now established himself amongst British scientists of the day as champion of popular science education in the field of natural history and as expert in museum work as part of general educational provision. In September 1854, the General Committee of the Liverpool Meeting of the British Association adopted a proposal[41] designed to improve provincial museums generally—

> "That Professor Henslow, Professor Phillips, Sir William Jarding, Mr. C. C. Babington, Professor E. Forbes, Professor Balfour, Professor Owen, Dr. Hooker, Mr. J. Scott Bowerbank, Rev. M. J. Berkeley, Dr. G. Johnston, Mr. Huxley, and Dr. Lankester be requested to draw up a report on the best manner of selecting and arranging a series of Typical Objects illustrative of the three kingdoms of Nature, for provincial Museums; with £10 at their disposal for the purpose."

In June of the next year Henslow circulated the committee for "names and addresses of naturalists whom they knew have paid special attention to particular groups in either animal, vegetable or mineral kingdoms".[42] He requested that "returns be made as speedily as convenient" and it was remarkable that many of the lists were available for report at the Glasgow Meeting in September 1855. The naturalists' replies and lists of suggested "Typical Objects" were included in the committee's report[43] for that year together with T. H. Huxley's information which was received as the report went to print. A further £10 was allocated to the committee who were "requested to print 250 copies of their Report on the Typical Forms for Museums, for distribution". The report, though not quite complete, formed an invaluable guide to other provincial museums whose work was still at the developmental stage.

Henslow himself was justly pleased with the Ipswich Museum. Characteristically he sought to share his enthusiasm with his family and close friends. Knights, the curator, received warning of some of these visitors by letter:

"28 May, 1855

. . . I may well get to Ipswich on Thursday for a few hours. If I come it will be with a bearded cousin, just to show him the Museum and one of my daughters."

"18th June 1855

I am expecting my friends on Monday with my second son. We shall be a party of four in our crag visiting. I think the best way will be to visit the Pleistocene beds about Colchester on the Tuesday, and then on to Ipswich on Wednesday."

A further note about this visit asked Knights to leave the key at the museum attendant's house as the party would arrive late in the evening, 8.10 at Ipswich.

Considerably later, when the museum was well developed, he persuaded his brother-in-law to visit it once more. Jenyns had seen the Institution on the occasion of the Ipswich British Association meeting six years previously. Jenyns' approval was important to Henslow[44] who expressed his simple satisfaction to Knights on 1st August admitting that "Jenyns was much pleased with the museum."

Perhaps more important to the prosperity of the museum was the result of a visit later in the month by a Treasury official, acquaintance of his son-in-law at Kew. Knights was again kept informed of the opinions passed.

"27th August 1857

. . . Dr. Hooker tells me Mr. Sully of the Treasury lately visited the Museum and expressed him much pleased with it.

(J.S.H.)"

*   *   *

Henslow saw the museum not only as a place where exhibits were available for all who wished to learn but also as a centre in which science could be taught and discussed. To this end he continued to take an active part in the programme of the museum lectures giving them priority even in his most busy years.

A pattern developed whereby Henslow normally lectured twice in the winter programme thus allowing time for lecture preparation after the Hitcham fetes were over and keeping clear of the summer term and the resumption of his Cambridge duties.

One of his first lectures at the Museum was not surprisingly a "Lecture on the Study of Botany". A handbill[45] dated 28th November had been sent to Thomas Martin and bore the accompanying information that two hundred tickets had been sent to Ipswich Young Men's Association. An audience must have been assured!

The organisers need not have had doubt about Henslow's capacity to attract and hold an audience and the subsequent records contain repeated attempts to encourage him to give more lectures than he was free to give. Even in the early years it proved difficult for Henslow to fit the lectures in but, as outside commitments crowded upon the man, he became less and less anxious to leave his Hitcham work-base. His difficulties are expressed in letters to close friends. Bree had invited the professor to give a lecture in the Stowmarket area and, while obviously loathe to refuse, Henslow spelled out his difficulties in reply, 15th November 1851.[46] Time for adequate preparation was just not available.

"I have undertaken to rewrite my volume of Botany in Lardiners' Cyclopaedia[47] against time, and really have not a moment to spare to get up anything for a lecture—If I had not promised them a Museum Lecture at Ipswich this week I should not have given one and have been obliged to refuse both Colchester and Bury. This whole week has been lost to my book by preparing diagrams, lecturing and attending as Income Tax Commissioner . . ."

He then suggests a compromise whereby Bree himself, together with one of Henslow's sisters from Woodbridge, might gather the illustrative materials together,

". . . and I could come over in the evening at the risk of a sore throat and resay what little I have to say on the subject".

He continued to lecture in Ipswich Museum in spite of all difficulties. By 1855, the pressures of work were becoming unbearable. At home, too, his mother was desperately ill and he and his wife had moved temporarily to Bildeston to be with her. This was the year too when he contributed an exhibit to the Paris Exhibition, and had embarked on a survey of museum material for the British Association. In the autumn he wrote to Knights as a desperately tired man and one for whom the expectations of an extra Museum lecture had just proved too much. The letter is produced at length for only thus can the full impact of the demands upon him and their consequent distress to him be conveyed.

"My dear Knights,

I write in a great hurry having done nothing for the last 3 days (and almost nights) but get ready a set of specimens for a lecture and demonstration at Stamford. I have now finished the job and packed up. I must seriously protest against the lecture programme. I understood very distinctly that I was to have 3 lectures assigned to me and that I might exchange one with Lord Arthur Harvey. I told you I should not be able this year to prepare the lecture on 'Botanical Geography', and Sidney was to take that day which comes too near my Cambridge lectures for me to think of lecturing then. I have now made other arrangements; I have engaged to lecture at Bury on March 4th and Lord Arthur Harvey is to lecture for me on January 22nd, but above all I have engaged with Lord Standley and the Department of Science and Art to prepare them 10 or 12 diagrams this winter which I could not have done if I had to prepare 4 lectures, and shall be pressed to do so with 2. I have so many calls on my time. Pray, therefore, strike out April 1st lecture, and if Sidney has declined for that day I will do my best to get someone to substitute. The Stamford job has set me 3 days behind, and made me half ill and now I am sent for to go to Lavenham to inspect a set of minerals for sale—and then something else will turn up, as generally does once and a half per day that I can't find time really for what I consent to do and must not take more upon me.

Surely there must be someone in Ipswich who can be persuaded to give us a lift. Excuse hurried letter.

Yours truly,"

The name of Lord Arthur as a substitute lecturer at Ipswich is interesting for he was yet another of the eminent scientists listed as subscribers to the museum following the 1851 British Association meeting in the town. Poor Knights had some difficulties over this substitution. Henslow in his agitation had told Harvey the incorrect date. All finally resolved itself however but Professor Henslow was forced to trade one lecture for another. Harvey thus agreed to address Ipswich Museum audience for him in the February, but Professor Henslow found himself addressing a group at the Athenaeum on 4th March 1856, on "Silica and its Abundance and Uses", under the Chairmanship of Lord Arthur Harvey himself. Henslow disliked lecturing outside the East Anglian area and felt London had scientific culture enough. A complimentary notice of the event reached Knights apparently without comment.

Evidently, Henslow was less harassed the following autumn when his various national tasks were completed and decided early in November upon the subject of his Ipswich lectures and set about seeking illustrative materials for them. A matter-of-fact note to Knights informed him of his decision,

> "About my 2 promised lectures . . . I will set to work to prepare for
> *Lecture 1* On the dependence of animals for organic compounds prepared by plants for the support of life.
> *Lecture 2* On popular error corrected by Natural Science."

The museum staff, sensing less pressure on the professor and responding to popular request, renewed the appeal for an extra lecture from him next season. The reply written on 1st August, 1857, was prompt and negative. It expressed clearly the importance Henslow gave to adequate preparation of his work.

> "I simply cannot do it, I would not use an old lecture, and to write a new one would take one three days besides the preparation of diagrams and specimens."

There is evidence enough in this simple statement, and in the unceasing demands for his lectures, to show the care with which he approached this aspect of popular science education, even in the busiest years of his life. His determination that the museum lectures should be worthwhile, relevant, appealing in content, meticulously prepared and generously illustrated reveal Henslow's concern for his subject, and the respect for the people he addressed.[48]

In return, the town of Ipswich was sincerely grateful to the professor and aware of his generosity and commitment on their behalf. Their appreciation of Henslow's talents in building up this educational museum for the townsfolk was expressed by the Mayor[49] who thanked the hardworking president of the museum, "not only for his most valuable series of lectures, which form but a very small part of the benefits he has conferred on the town but for the indefatigable attention which he has given to the interests of the Museum, in preparing and arranging many cases full of specimens, models and diagrams as types of different classes of matter and his attention in seeing them properly arranged."

NOTE: Many of the original cases remain in Ipswich Museum today. This is interesting to the historian, yet sad also. Towards the end of the industrial revolution, Ipswich lost many of its richer burghers to the County of Suffolk and the town museum along with other municipal amenities was less generously provided for. The economic and social fortunes of this institution have varied, but its sound scientific base remains. Perhaps the time has come for a revival of fortunes to facilitate a contemporary response to the demands of a more educated and more demanding public.

CHAPTER NINE

A Reflection

TODAY, Hitcham's churchtower dominates a peaceful, prosperous and well-husbanded countryside, contrasting dramatically with the depressed district first encountered by Henslow in 1837. Within the church door, an illuminated roll of parish rectors simply records the stewardship of John Stevens Henslow, 1837-1861. Uniquely, on the wall between the door and the south window and above the font hangs a portrait of the Reverend Professor. And so this exceptional priest and scientist seems even yet to look benignly upon the parishioners as they settle in their pews.

In the village itself the original schoolroom has long since disappeared and the Hitcham children now attend a modern school at Bildeston. The old rectory and the lovely lawns that once bore the traffic of Hitcham's famous horticultural shows and pyrotechnic displays are now in private hands. Yet Henslow's name is legend still amongst the long-established families of the village. They affectionately recount tales of the eminent Cambridge science professor who learned to love the land and the people who worked upon it; who fought to bring skills and self-respect to the agricultural labourers; whose educational provisions and encouragement brought old and young alike nearer to the realisation of their potential; and whose wide-ranging scientific knowledge was shared with all who had ears to hear, skill to read or eyes to see.

Henslow's influence on science education beyond his immediate parish is harder to assess. His pamphlet,[1] botanical-drawings and simple instructional apparatus exhibited at South Kensington from 1858 enabled others to learn of his successful classroom methods. Records indeed show that where botany entered the English schools Henslow's methods of teaching were frequently employed. The publication by the British Association of Henslow's report *On Typical Forms of Minerals, Plants and Animals for Museums*, 1856, ensured that the Henslow model for an instructional natural history museum (as exemplified at Ipswich) was available to curators seeking to develop successful educational museums. At Cambridge, the mature botanic gardens and museums stand testimony to his vision and industry. The bust of the professor at Kew reminds the nation of his contribution to the national botany museum and herbarium there.

It was at individual level, however, that Henslow most encouraged potential scientists whether they be school children, pupil teachers, farmers, labourers, students or friends to pursue their work with diligence and enthusiasm. The words of Sir Joseph Dalton Hooker, a British botanist of national eminence and international repute, are chosen as final tribute to this exceptional teacher. Hooker humbly attributed much of his own scientific progress to the constant and kindly guidance of John Stevens Henslow, his friend and father-in-law whom he had attended in the last weeks of his illness. On 23rd May 1861, the day after the simple burial service for Henslow at Hitcham, Hooker wrote to a close friend[2] admitting his great indebtedness to the late professor and of his sense of personal loss,

"Henslow has left a blank in my existence never to be replaced. Quite apart from considerations matrimonial Henslow had more influence over my life and conduct than any other man, so good, so calm, so wise, so far above all taint of pride, prejudice or passion, so magnanimous in short was he in all situations in life. More than all this, I miss his knowledge of loads of matters bearing on Botany which I never knew nor took up but through him, and of loads of kindred subjects in which I have keenly interested myself, ever since I knew him. He was one of those friends found late in life to be a lamp unto our path . . ."

Appendix I

Among the fellow scientists whose names occur in the Henslow story are:—

BABINGTON, Charles (1808-1895). Professor of Botany, Cambridge, after Henslow's death, 1861. (Student and colleague of Henslow's at Cambridge.)

BERKELEY, Miles J. (1803-1889). Cryptogamic botanist (attended Henslow's classes at Cambridge).

BOWERBANK, James Scott (1797-1877). Geologist and one time lecturer in botany. Partner in London distillery.

DARWIN, Charles (1809-1882). Author of *Origin of Species*, etc. (Student of Henslow's at Cambridge.)

DAWES, Richard (1793-1867). Dean of Hereford 1850. Contemporary of Henslow's at Cambridge. Mathematical tutor and bursar of Downing College. Founded a model parish school in Kings Somborne 1842—natural science taught there.

FORBES, Edward (1815-1854). Naturalist. Professor of Botany at King's College, London 1842. President of Geological Society 1853 and earlier lecturer to that Society.

GRAY, John E. (1800-1875). Keeper of Zoological section at the British Museum.

HOOKER, Joseph (1817-1911). Eminent botanist (married Henslow's third daughter).

HOOKER, William J. (1785-1865). Director of Royal Gardens, Kew, from 1841.

JENYNS, Leonard (1800-1893). Botanist. Fellow student with Henslow at Cambridge (Henslow married his sister, Harriet, 1823).

KIRBY, William (1759-1850). Entomologist. Author of *Bridgewater Treatise*. Friend of Henslow's at Cambridge. Vicar of Barham, Suffolk.

LANKESTER, Edwin (1814-1874). Secretary to Ray Club 1844. Professor of Natural History, New College, London. Examiner in Botany for Science and Art Department 1862.

LINDLEY, John (1799-1865). Botanist and horticulturalist. Professor of Botany at University College, London, 1829. (Editor of *Gardeners' Chronicle*.)

LYELL, Charles (1797-1875). Author of *Principles of Geology*, 1830. Professor of Geology, King's College, London, 1831-3. President of Geological Society 1835-6, 1849-50.

MARTIN, Thomas (1779-1867). F.R.C.S., General Practitioner, Reigate. Founder of Mechanics' Institute, Reigate, 1830. Founded local benefit societies. Supported foundation and development of local National schools.

OWEN, Richard (1804-1892). Hunterian Professor of Comparative Anatomy at Royal College of Surgeons 1836-56. In charge of Natural History departments of British Museum.

PLAYFAIR, Lyon (1818-1898). Member of Executive Committee for Great Exhibition 1851 and Secretary for Science in Department of Science and Art, 1853. Prepared English edition of Liebig's work on Agricultural Chemistry.

REEVE, Lovell Augustus (1814-1865). Conchologist. Acted as conchologist to Natural History section of British Association's excursion to fens. Opened a shop in King William Street, Strand, for sale of Natural History specimens.

SEDGWICK, Adam (1785-1873). Professor of Geology at Cambridge from 1818. President of British Association 1833. Cambridge Secretary to Prince Albert, Chancellor of Cambridge University, from 1847. (Godfather to Henslow's daughter, Mrs Barnard.)

WHEWELL, William (1794-1866). Professor of Moral Philosophy and Master of Trinity, Cambridge from 1841. Vice-Chancellor 1842-3. Author of *History of Inductive Sciences*, 1837 and *Philosophy of the Inductive Sciences*, 1840.

Appendix II

HONORARY MEMBERS OF THE IPSWICH MUSEUM.

PUBLISHED

By GEORGE RANSOME, F.L.S., etc., Hon. Sec.

Dedicated, with Permission, to Her Majesty the Queen and H.R.H. Prince Albert.

HIS ROYAL HIGHNESS PRINCE ALBERT, K.G., F.R.S., Patron of the Ipswich Museum.

GEORGE BIDDELL AIRY, M.A., D.C.L., F.R.S., Astronomer Royal.

GEORGE ALLMAN, M.D., F.R.C.S.I., M.R.I.A., etc., Professor of Botany in the University of Dublin, Examiner in Zoology and Botany in the Queen's University in Ireland, Author of *'Biological Contributions,' 'Report on Fresh-water Polyzoa,'* etc.

DAVID THOMAS ANSTED, F.R.S. and G.S., Professor of Geology in King's College, Author of *'The Ancient World,' 'Elementary Course of Geology,'* etc.

ROBERT BALL, LL.D., F.R.I.A., Sec. R.Z.S., Director of the Dublin University Museum, Secretary to the Queen's University in Ireland, Author of Papers on the *Phocidæ, Cephalopoda,* Fossil Oxen and Fossil Bears found in Ireland.

SIR HENRY T. DE LA BECHE, C.B., F.R.S., F.G.S., etc., Director-General of the Geological Survey of the United Kingdom, Author of *'Researches in Theoretical Geology,' 'The Geological Observer,'* etc.

THOMAS BELL, Sec. R.S., Professor of Zoology in King's College, Vice-President of the Ipswich Museum, Author of *'History of British Reptiles,' 'British Crustacea,'* etc.

SIR JOHN P. BOILEAU, BART., F.R.S., Vice-President of the Ipswich Museum.

CHARLES LUCIEN BONAPARTE, PRINCE OF CANINO, Author of *'Fauna Italica,' 'Continuation of Wilson's Ornithology,* etc.

JAMES SCOTT BOWERBANK, F.R.S., L.S., and G.S., Author of *'Fossil Fruits and Seeds,'* etc.

THE MOST NOBLE THE MARQUIS OF BRISTOL, F.R.S., Patron of the Ipswich Museum.

ROBERT BROWN, D.C.L., F.R.S., Pres. L.S., etc., Author of *'Prodromus Floræ Novæ Hollandiæ,'* etc.

JOHN LEE, LL.D., F.R.A.S., Author of *'Antiquarian Researches in the Ionian Islands,'* and Founder of the Hartwell Observatory.

JOHN LINDLEY, Phil. D., F.R.S. and L.S., Professor of Botany, Univ. Coll., London, Author of *'The Vegetable Kingdom,' 'School Botany,'* etc.

SIR CHARLES LYELL, M.A., F.R.S. and L.S., President of the Geological Society, Vice-President of the Ipswich Museum, Author of *'Principles of Geology,' 'Travels in North America,'* etc.

DAVID WILLIAM MITCHELL, B.A., F.L.S., Secretary of the Zoological Society of London, Illustrator of *'The Genera of Birds.'*

SIR RODERICK IMPEY MURCHISON, M.A., F.R.S. and L.S., V.P.G.S., Hon. Mem. R.S. Ed. and R.I.A., M. Imp. Ac. Sc. St. Petersb., Corr. Mem. Inst. Fr., R. Ac. Ber., Tur., etc., Author of *'The Silurian System,' 'The Geology of Russia and the Ural Mountains, Alps, Apennines, and Carpathians,'* etc.

RICHARD OWEN, V.P.R.S., F.G.S., etc., Hunterian Professor of Comparative Anatomy in the College of Surgeons, Vice-President of the Ipswich Museum, Author of *'History of British Fossil Mammals and Birds,' 'Memoir of the Pearly Nautilus,'* etc.

ROBERT PATTERSON, V.P. Nat. Hist. and Phil. Soc. Belfast, Author of *'Zoology for Schools,'* etc.

JOHN PHILLIPS, F.R.S. and G.S., Professor of Geology, Author of *'Geology of the Mountain Limestone,' 'Geology of the Yorkshire Coast,'* etc.

LYON PLAYFAIR, C.B., F.R.S., etc., Chemist to the Museum of Practical Geology, Author of *'Report on the State of Large Towns in the Manufacturing Districts,'* and various Chemical Memoirs.

JAMES RANSOME, Hon. Mem. Ipswich Museum.

VERY REV. WILLIAM BUCKLAND, D.D., F.R.S., L.S., and G.S., Corr. Mem. Inst. Fr., and Vice-President of the Ipswich Museum, Professor of Geology, Oxford, Dean of Westminster, Author of 'Reliquiæ Diluvianæ,' 'Bridgewater Treatise,' etc. (From a daguerreotype by Claudet.)

WILLIAM CARPENTER, M.D., F.R.S. and G.S., Author of 'Animal Physiology,' 'Report on the Microscopic Structure of Shells,' etc.

SIR WILLIAM CUBITT, F.R.S., M.R.I.A., F.R.A.S., etc., President of the Institution of Civil Engineers.

JOHN CURTIS, F.L.S., Author of 'British Entomology.'

EDWARD DOUBLEDAY, F.L.S., Author of 'The Genera of Lepidoptera.'

CHARLES DARWIN, M.A., F.R.S. and G.S., Author of 'Journal of a Naturalist,' etc.

MICHAEL FARADAY, D.C.L., F.R.S., Fullerian Professor of Chemistry in the Royal Institution of Great Britain, Author of 'Chemical Manipulation,' and numerous Papers in the Philosophical Transactions.

EDWARD FORBES, F.R.S. and G.S., Professor of Botany in King's College, Vice-President of the Ipswich Museum, Author of 'History of British Star-fishes,' 'Essay on the Origin of the British Fauna and Flora,' etc.

EDWARD FORSTER, F.R.S., V.P.L.S., Author of Papers on British Botany.

JOHN GOULD, F.R.S. and L.S., Author of 'Birds of Europe,' 'Birds of Australia,' etc.

ROBERT EDMOND GRANT, M.D., F.R.S., Professor of Comparative Anatomy and Zoology in University College, Author of 'Outlines of Comparative Anatomy,' etc.

JOHN EDWARD GRAY, F.R.S. and G.S., Keeper of the Zoological Department of the British Museum, Author of numerous Zoological Papers.

WILLIAM HENRY HARVEY, M.D., Professor of Botany to the Dublin Society, Author of 'History of British Sea-weeds,' 'The Sea-side Book,' etc.

REV. DR. HINDS, BISHOP OF NORWICH, Patron of the Ipswich Museum.

REV. J. S. HENSLOW, M.A., F.L.S. and G.S., Professor of Botany, Cambridge, President of the Ipswich Museum, Author of 'Principles of Descriptive and Physiological Botany,' etc.

SIR WILLIAM JACKSON HOOKER, D.C.L., F.R.S., L.S., and G.S., Director of the Royal Gardens of Kew, Author of 'The British Flora,' 'Curtis's Botanical Magazine,' etc.

JOSEPH DALTON HOOKER, M.D., F.R.S., L.S., and G.S., Author of 'The Botany of the Antarctic Voyage.'

SIR WILLIAM JARDINE, BART., F.R.S.E. and L.S., etc., Vice-President of the Ipswich Museum, Author of 'The Naturalist's Library,' 'Contributions to Ornithology,' etc.

REV. WILLIAM KIRBY, M.A., F.R.S., L.S., and G.S., late President of the Ipswich Museum, Author of 'An Introduction to Entomology,' 'Bridgewater Treatise,' etc.

GENERAL SIR EDWARD KERRISON, BART., K.C.B., Hon. Mem. Ipswich Museum.

EDWIN LANKESTER, M.D., F.R.S. and L.S., V.P. London Med. Soc., Professor of Natural History in New College, London, and Translator of Schleiden's 'Principles of Scientific Botany.'

LOVELL REEVE, F.L.S., Corr. Mem. Nat. Hist. Soc. Wirtemberg and New York, Author of 'Conchologia, Systematica,' 'Conchologia Iconica,' 'Geographical Distribution of Land Mollusca,' etc.

REV. STEPHEN J. RIGAUD, M.A., F.R.A.S., Editor of Correspondence of Newton and his Contemporaries.'

RIGHT HON. LORD RENDLESHAM, M.P., Vice-President of the Ipswich Museum.

SIR JAMES CLARKE ROSS, Capt. R.N., D.C.L., F.R.S. and L.S., Author of 'Voyage to the Southern Seas,' etc.

LIEUTENANT-COLONEL EDWARD SABINE, V.P.R.S., F.R.A.S., Corr. Mem. Imp. Acad. St. Petersburg, etc.

REV. ADAM SEDGWICK, F.R.S. and G.S., Woodwardian Professor of Geology in the University of Cambridge, Vice-President of the Ipswich Museum, Author of 'A Discourse on the Studies of the University of Cambridge,' 'Remarks on the Structure of Large Mineral Mosses,' etc.

PRIDEAUX JOHN SELBY, F.L.S. and G.S., M.W.S., Author of 'British Ornithology,' 'British Forest Trees,' etc.

REV. EDWIN SIDNEY, M.A., Vice-President of the Ipswich Museum, Author of 'Blights of the Wheat and their Remedies,' 'Electricity, its Phenomena, Laws,' etc.

WILLIAM SPENCE, F.R.S. and L.S., V.P. Ent. Soc., Vice-President of the Ipswich Museum, Author of 'An Introduction to Entomology,' etc.

REV. DR. STANLEY, F.R.S., Pres. L.S., late Bishop of Norwich, and Patron of the Ipswich Museum.

RICHARD TAYLOR, Under Secretary L.S., F.R.A.S., F.S.A., Mem. Nat. Hist. Soc. Mosc., Author of Notes and Additions to Tooke's 'Diversions of Parley' and to Warton's 'History of English Poetry.'

WILLIAM THOMPSON, President Nat. Hist. and Phil. Soc. Belfast, Author of 'The Birds of Ireland,' etc.

NATHANIEL WALLICH, M.D., F.R.S.L. and E., F.L.S. and G.S., Author of 'Plantæ Asiaticæ Rariores,' etc.

GEORGE R. WATERHOUSE, V.P. Entomological Society, Author of 'History of the Mammalia,' etc.

JOHN O. WESTWOOD, F.L.S., Pres. Ent. Soc., Corr. Mem. Nat. Hist. Soc., Lund., Boston, U.S., etc.: Author of 'An Introduction to the Modern Classification of Insects,' Arcana Entomologica,' etc.

WILLIAM YARRELL, V.P.L.S. and Z.S., Vice-President of the Ipswich Museum, Author of 'History of British Birds,' 'History of British Fishes,' etc.

T. B. WESTERN, ESQ., Vice-President of the Ipswich Museum.

IPSWICH,
1852.

References

CHAPTER ONE   The Man, His Times and His Task

1. *Gentleman's Magazine*, July 1861—"Obituary of Reverend John Stevens Henslow".
2. Jenyns, Leonard, *Memoir of the Reverend John Stevens Henslow, M.A., F.L.S., F.G.S., F.C.P.S.*, 1862.
   Chapter 1 gives an account of Henslow's school and student days.
3. Clark and Hughes, *Life and Letters of Adam Sedgwick, Vol. II*, 1890, p. 402.
4. Biographical Sketch of the Reverend John Stevens Henslow in *Gardeners' Chronicle*, 1861.
5. Henslow, J. S., "A Reformer's Duty—An Address to the Reformers of the Town of Cambridge", 1837 in Cambridge University Library.
   Details of Henslow's part in a number of Cambridge campaigns are recorded in Jenyns' *Memoir* and further accounts appear in Clark and Hughes *Life and Letters of Adam Sedgwick, Vol. I*, 1890.
6. A copy of the sermon is to be found in Cambridge University Library.
7. His views on the reconciliation of pursuit of science with religious belief is clearly expressed in his "Address to members of the University of Cambridge on the expediency of improving and on the funds required for remodelling and supporting the Botany Gardens", 1846.
   A copy is held by Cambridge University Library.

CHAPTER TWO   A Cambridge Apprenticeship

1. Next to him on the Tripos list was Alex Ramsey, with whom Henslow was friendly in his postgraduate years. Other close acquaintances of those days were Dawes (mathematician), Kirby (entomologist) and Jenyns (botanist), all of whom figure in later chapters of this book.
2. Details of Henslow's life at Cambridge are recorded by his brother-in-law, L. Jenyns, in his *Memoirs of the Rev. John Stevens Henslow*, 1862, Chapter 3.
3. Report of the survey was given to the Cambridge Philosophical Society in November 1821 and is recorded in *Cambridge Philosophical Transactions*, Vol. 1.
4. *A Syllabus of a Course of Lectures on Mineralogy*, Cambridge 1823. A copy is held by Cambridge University Library.
5. "Biographical Sketch of the Reverend John Stevens Henslow" (reprinted from the *Gardeners' Chronicle*), 1861. Copy in British Museum.
6. The numbers dropped dramatically after Henslow left Cambridge for Hitcham, so did the interest of senior members. Babington wrote to Professor Balfour 2nd June 1846, in depressed tones,
   "Never was botany at so low an ebb as now in this place. A non-resident Professor, who only comes here five weeks (as he calls it), going away on Saturday morning each week, and returning Monday evening. I have been taking a party of our few naturalists for a short excursion on each of the last few Saturdays, but never got more than twelve to accompany me, all of them quite beginners."
   Quoted from *Charles Cardale Babington Memorials, Journal and Botanical Correspondence of*, 1897, p. 297.

7. Jenyns, *op. cit.* pp. 38-9.
8. Henslow, J. S. *Collection of Letters and Notices* in Cambridge University Botany Department Library.
9. Charles Cardale Babington, *op. cit.* pp. 3-4.
10. L. Jenyns, *op. cit.* p. 39.
11. Babington was one who attended successive courses and records on 22nd April 1833 "Henslow commenced his lectures; this is the sixth course I have attended". See C. C. Babington, *op. cit.* p. 16.
12. Darwin, C. "Recollections of J.S.H." in F. Darwin, *Life and Letters of Charles Darwin, Volume I*, 1887.
13. C. Darwin's "Autobiography" in F. Darwin *op. cit.* p. 48.
14. Barlow, N. (ed.) *Darwin and Henslow* 1967, Letter 27, p. 77.
15. Babington, C. C. *op. cit.* Gamlingay visits are entered in *Journal* for years 1833-36, 1838-41, 1845, 1847-1850, 1851.
16. F. Darwin *op. cit.* p. 188.
17. *Ibid.*
18. Babington *op. cit.* p. 60.
19. C. Darwin's "Autobiography" in F. Darwin *op. cit.* p. 52.
20. "Recollections of J.S.H." in F. Darwin *op. cit.* p. 187.
21. Taken from "Notice by Mr. Berkeley" in Jenyns *op. cit.* p. 56.
22. Henslow was ordained priest in 1824 and acted as curate at Little St Mary's Cambridge. In 1832, he was given a living by Lord Brougham at Cholsey-cum-Moulsford, Berkshire but lived there only in the vacations. In 1837, he was presented with the remunerable crown living at Hitcham to which he moved in 1839. His stimulating influence at Cambridge was sadly missed—see D. A. Winstanley, *Early Victorian Cambridge*, 1955, p. 181. See also C. C. Babington *op. cit.* p. 297.
23. The quote is taken from *Biographical Sketch of the Rev. J. S. Henslow*, 1861, reprinted from the *Gardeners' Chronicle*. The author was probably Professor J. Lindley, editor of the journal and Henslow's University of London colleague and close friend. Lindley gave considerable space in his journal to advertising Henslow's educational work during the Hitcham years and was a great admirer of his teaching skills.
24. In F. Darwin *op. cit.*
25. In F. Darwin *op. cit.*, p. 182.
26. *Biographical Sketch of the Rev. John Stevens Henslow*, 1861.
27. Thus Babington began to collect data for his *Manual of British Botany* in 1835 and was writing the first edition in 1843.
28. Peacock had the post of naturalist on the *Beagle* at his disposal and referred it to Henslow. Both Henslow and Jenyns had considered the *Beagle* appointment themselves but had decided against it. Henslow was asked to find a suitable person and selected Charles Darwin.
29. Charles Dickens "The Mudfog and other Sketches", 1836-37 in *Sketches by Boz.*
30. Henslow was made a Secretary in May 1821 after his appointment to a Chair and continued in office until he went to Hitcham to live permanently, in 1839.
31. Jenyns, *op. cit.*, p. 43.
32. The term was used of Henslow's work on Digitalis in the "Notice by Mr. Berkeley" incorporated in Jenyns, *op. cit.*, p. 56-7.
    Berkeley wrote of Henslow, the scientist,
    "He was, in fact, so completely free from prejudice, and so desirous of ascertaining the truth, and nothing but the truth, that he was the man of all others for such investigations, and I have always regretted that he gave so little time in after days to original researches."
33. Whewell, W., *Of Liberal Education in General and with particular reference to the Leading Studies of the University of Cambridge.* Cambridge, 1845.
34. *Darwin and Henslow: the growth of an idea.* Edited by Nora Barlow, London, 1967.

35. Professor Henslow chaired the Natural History section of the British Association for the Advancement of Science during the famous debate in Oxford, in June, 1860, where T. H. Huxley, supporting Darwin's theory and outraged by Bishop Wilberforce's "second-hand" arguments, expressed his preference for an ape as ancestor to a gifted man who distorted the truth!

"I must tell you", wrote Hooker to Darwin "that Henslow as President would have none speak but those who had arguments to use, and four speakers had been burked by the audience (700) and President for mere declamation."

See account in L. Huxley, *Life and Letters of Joseph Dalton Hooker*, Vol. 1, 1918, pp. 520-527.

36. C. Darwin's "Autobiography" in F. Darwin, *op. cit.*, p. 56.

37. They accused Darwin of "departing from the spirit of inductive philosophy". See Darwin's letter to Henslow 8th May 1860 in N. Barlow, *op. cit.*, p. 204.

38. L. Huxley, *Life and Letters of Joseph Dalton Hooker*, Vol. I, 1918, pp. 512-3.

39. Letter from Professor Henslow, January 1861, printed in *MacMillan's Magazine* No. 16, Vol. IV, February, 1861.

40. Barlow, N., *op. cit.*, Letter 113, p. 206.

41. The *Bridgewater Treatises* published between 1835 and 1840 embodied the main arguments of scientists of the day. Two of Henslow's friends William Whewell and William Kirby were contributors.

42. Suggestions for a Natural Science Tripos and Moral Science Tripos were "persuaded by Prince Albert [Chancellor] and worked on by others including Dr. Whewell". See Winstanley, *op. cit.*, p. 209.

43. A copy is held in Cambridge University Library.

44. The arrival of overseas flora in the botany departments of Oxford and Cambridge at this time gave opportunity for pressing the urgent cause of scientific study where it was still held in relatively low account. Sir William Hooker expressed hope that recent offers of valuable plant collections to the two universities would rouse interest in science. He wrote to Bentham on 5th February, 1852.

"Legacies may be the means of instilling new life into the Universities; the conditions being reasonable. A proper recognition backed perhaps by P.A. (Prince Albert) as Chancellor, with the offer of such a herbarium as Fielding's of Lehmann's should do wonders . . ."

This quotation is taken from the letter in L. Huxley's *Life and Letters of Joseph Dalton Hooker*, 1918, Vol. I, p. 382.

45. see Jenyns, *op. cit.*, p. 120-1 and C. C. Babington, *op. cit.*, p. 174.

46. Jenyns, *op. cit.*

47. *Syllabus of Lectures on Botany for a Pass examination*, 1848 (Copies are held in the British Museum and Cambridge University Libraries). It includes structural, systematic and physiological botany and has an appendix outlining the demonstration of fourteen common plants.

48. Winstanley, D. A. *Early Victorian Cambridge*, 1955, p. 210.

49. *Questions on the Subject Matter of Sixteen Lectures in Botany required for a Pass-examination*, 1851. A copy is held by Cambridge University Library.

50. Jenyns, *op. cit.*, p. 39.

51. Henslow, George, *Reminiscences of a Scientific Suffolk Clergyman*, No. I, in *Eastern Counties Magazine and Suffolk Notebook*, 1900.

CHAPTER THREE   The Parish School and other Charities

1. *Biographical Sketch of the Reverend John Stevens Henslow*. (Reprinted from the *Gardeners' Chronicle*), London 1861, p. 10.

2. *Ibid.*, p. 22.

3. Jenyns, *op. cit.*, p. 69.

4. Glyde, *Suffolk in the Nineteenth Century*, 1851. Social background information for Suffolk at this time is largely derived from this volume.
5. *Parish Accounts*, 1841 in *Hitcham Papers* deposited in Ipswich Public Library.
6. *Ibid.*
7. Henslow, George, *Reminiscences of a Scientific Suffolk Clergyman*, 1901, No. VI.
8. *Darwin and Henslow*, p. 167.
9. *Ibid.*, p. 166.
10. Henslow, G., *Reminiscences*, 1900
11. *School Report* 1854 in *Hitcham Papers* at Ipswich Public Library.
12. *Parish Accounts*, 1841.
13. Henslow's letter to parishioners, 25th November 1841, introducing *Parish Accounts* for 1841 and included with *Hitcham Papers* at Ipswich Public Library.
14. The National Society mentioned in the above letter was together with the British and Foreign School Society, responsible for the provision of most elementary schools of that time. The National Society concerned itself with Church of England schools and the British and Foreign School Society with non-conformist schools. Both were founded for promoting Christian elementary education for the labouring classes up and down the country and the eligibility of a school for a share of the annual Government grant (£36,000 was first made available in 1830) was determined principally by the private subscriptions it could raise in aid. Thus the National Society's injunction to parishioners to be generous.
15. *Parish Accounts*, 1842/3.
16. *Ibid.*
17. Henslow, J. S. *Two Sermons preached First and Eighth of January, 1843—In aid of a Parish School, and certain clubs established for the assistance and relief of the poor*, p. 32.
    A copy is included in the *Hitcham Parish Records*.
18. A Henslow manuscript in Ipswich Public Library written in July 1844, records:
    "I very lately summoned the unemployed labourers of this parish to meet me and between 20 and 30 of them assembled. I then read to them letters from Newcastle in which they were offered wages from 3/- to 4/- per day in the collieries. I engaged they should have all befitting arrangements made for them both at starting from Ipswich and again upon their arrival at Newcastle. They were even offered to be sent back again at the end of the month free of expenses if they did not like their quarters. Not one of them would stir! A wholly uneducated and uninformed agricultural labourer is sometimes more like an animal guided by mere instinct than man directed by reason.
19. *Two Sermons*, pp. 33-4.
20. *Parish Accounts*, 1844.
21. *Two Sermons etc.*, p. 26.
22. Quote from *Bury Post* incorporated in Henslow's *School Report*, 1854, in *Hitcham Papers* at Ipswich Public Library.
23. Glyde, *op. cit.*, p. 360.
24. *Ibid.*, p. 228.
25. *Parish Accounts*, 1852 Subscriptions amounted to a mere £13 17s 6d. To qualify for the grant £52.00 was necessary in subscriptions (40 girls and 40 boys).
26. Of the subscriptions (£53 19s 0d) for 1858, £31 came from the Henslow family.
27. *Henslow's Letters* filed in University of Cambridge Botany Library.
28. *School Report*, 1854 in *Hitcham Papers* at Ipswich Public Library.
29. *Ibid.*
30. Jenyns, *op. cit.*, p. 100-107. See also Chapters 3 and 4 below.
31. *Henslow Letters*, 1850-1858, at Ipswich Museum.
32. *Ibid.*
33. *Parish Accounts*, 1859.
34. *Ibid.*
35. *Memorandum*—a copy is included in *Henslow's Letters*, 1850-1858, kept at Ipswich Museum.

36. Feoffment Charity Record Book in *Hitcham Parish Records.*
37. *Ibid.*
38. Messrs Ransome of the famous iron works at Ipswich. Henslow made their acquaintance through his work at the Museum at Ipswich. George Ransome was Hon. Sec. of the Museum for some time. The Ransome family assisted Henslow in a number of ways. In addition to subscribing to his school, they entertained his villagers when they went to Ipswich on a number of summer day excursions. (See later Chapter Five.)
39. *Hitcham Papers.*
40. Quoted in a manuscript (probably in Glyde's hand) in *Hitcham Papers.*

CHAPTER FOUR   Botany Teaching in a Village School

1. Detail of the early lessons and the schedule were described by Henslow in detail in a series of articles in the *Gardeners' Chronicle,* 1856. This annual was edited by Professor Lindley, of London University who was a great admirer of Henslow's efforts to bring science to the people of his area and assisted him in a number of practical ways. The two professors were colleagues for many years while Henslow acted as examiner for botany at London University and they had both worked with Sir William Hooker at Kew when the gardens were made over to the nation.
   Another useful account of these lessons is given by Henslow's botanist son, George, in *The Leisure Hour,* 1862.
   Henslow's own pamphlet for the Science and Art Department *Illustrations to be employed in practical Lessons on Botany; adapted to beginners of all classes,* published 1858 by Chapman and Hall was available in the British Museum Library. Leonard Jenyns quoted at length from this pamphlet in his *Memoirs of the Rev. John Stevens Henslow,* 1862.
2. See Bremner, J. P. *Some Aspects of the Teaching of Biological Sciences in English Schools during the Second Half of the Nineteenth Century,* 1955. Unpublished thesis in University of London Library.
3. See *schedule.*
4. *Henslow Letters, 1850-1858* in Ipswich Museum.
5. Henslow, G. "Practical Lessons in Systematic and Economic Botany" in the *Leisure Hour,* 1862, p. 677.
6. *Henslow Letters,* Ipswich Museum.
7. *Ibid.*
8. *Ibid.*
9. *School Reports,* 1854-1859, in *Hitcham Papers,* held in Ipswich Public Library.
10. Jenyns, *op. cit.,* p. 105.
11. *Ibid.,* p. 107.
12. Henslow, J. S. "Practical Lessons in Botany for Beginners of all Classes", No. 3 in *Gardeners' Chronicle,* 26th July 1856 held in Colindale Library. Some of the botanical walks took place "after divine service" and were joined by previous schoolpupils.
13. *Henslow Letters,* Ipswich Museum.
14. *Ibid.*
15. As the family explained, William's nickname Buffalo was given to him because he used to charge wildly round the countryside at the time when "Buffalo Bill" was all the rage.
16. Quoted from *Darwin and Henslow,* pp. 176-7.
17. *Ibid.,* pp. 180-1.
18. *Ib.,* p. 185.
19. *Ib.,* p. 188.
20. Huxley, L., *Life and Letters of Sir J. D. Hooker, Vol. I,* p. 395.
21. *Henslow Correspondence,* Kew Herbarium and Library.
22. Henslow kept two of the Treatises on his library shelves for villagers to borrow. The volumes had been written by his Cambridge friends W. Kirby and W. Whewell.

23. Quoted at length in Jenyns *Memoirs* and in part in Henslow, G. *Reminiscences etc. IV.*
24. Henslow, G. *Reminiscences etc. VIII.*
25. *Henslow Letters.*
26. Jenyns, *op. cit.,* p. 112.
27. Quoted in Henslow's *School Report,* 1860.
28. See Mitchell, Rev. M. "General Report for the Year 1858" in *Report of the Committee of Council on Education, 1858-9.*
29. The school of Faculty Psychology was fashionable at this time. George Combe was a leading exponent of this theory which held that the mind was made up of a number of "faculties"—such as "observation", "reasoning"—located in specified areas of the brain and capable of being individually trained. China models of the brain, showing supposed locations of the "faculties", were popular acquisitions for display in Victorian studies and even drawing rooms!
30. Henslow, Geo., *Reminiscences etc. VIII.* Quotation is taken from his father's "Sermon" preached in aid of the parish school, 1855.
31. Henslow, J. S., *Examples of Botany in Village Education* in *Gardeners' Chronicle,* 5th July 1856.
32. Henslow, J. S., *Practical Lessons in Botany for Beginners of all Classes IV,* in *Gardeners' Chronicle,* 2nd August, 1856. He had earlier used this argument in his *Address to the members of the University of Cambridge on the expediency of improving and on the funds required for remodelling and supporting the Botanic Gardens,* 1846, see Chapter Two above.
33. Whewell, W. *Of Liberal Education,* Cambridge 1845.
34. Patterson, Robert, *On the Study of Natural History as a Branch of General Education in Schools and Colleges,* 1840, p. 1.
35. *Darwin and Henslow,* p. 171.

CHAPTER FIVE   Botany Teaching and the Nation

1. Actually, it was Henslow's ex-student and successor to the Cambridge Chair, C. C. Babington, who modified the Henslow schedules for beginners by eliminating many of the technical terms. By 1869, Taunton College was already using Babington's modification of the Henslow schedules. See Tuckwell, Rev. W., "On the method of teaching physical science in schools, 1869". Appended statement to the *VIth Report of the Devonshire Commission.*
2. Walter Fitch, originally a pattern drawer in a calico factory, was official draughtsman for Kew botanical publications from 1834.
3. Letters quoted here are from *Rev. J. S. Henslow's Correspondence* at Kew Herbarium and Library.
4. *Henslow's Letters 1850-1858,* Ipswich Museum.
5. *Henslow's Correspondence,* Kew.
6. *Report of the Science and Art Department of the Committee of Council on Education 1858-9,* p. 37.
7. *Report of the Science and Art Department 1879.*
8. *Report of the Committee of Council on Education 1890.*
9. *Henslow's Correspondence,* Kew.
10. *Ibid.*
11. Henslow, J. S., "Botanical Lecturer to the Royal Family" in *Gardeners' Chronicle,* 14th July 1860.
12. *Ibid.*
13. *Ib.*
14. *Ib.*
15. *Henslow's Letters,* Ipswich Museum.
16. *Ibid.*
17. Henslow, J. S., *Report of the British Association for the Advancement of Science, 1859.*

18. Jenyns, *op. cit.*, p. 106.
19. Hooker, J. D., *General Evidence to Clarendon Commission*, pp. 382-6.
20. Wilson, J. M., *Notes on the Early History of Rugby School Natural History Society*, 1916.
21. *Report of Schools Inquiry Commission*, 1868, Vol. II, pp. 227-229.
22. Wilson, J. M., "On Teaching Natural Science in Schools", 1868 in *Essays on a Liberal Education*, ed. Farrar, 1868.
23. *Ibid.*
24. It is likely that Henslow was strengthened in his resolve to teach technical terms to beginners in botany by his Cambridge colleague, Dr Whewell, for whom the meaningful use of scientific terms was regarded as a major virtue of the study of botanical science.
25. Tuckwell, Rev. W., "On the method of teaching physical science in schools", 1869, appended to *VIth Report of the Devonshire Commission*.
26. *VIth Report of the Devonshire Commission*, 1875, Appendix II para 13.
27. *Ibid.*, Appendix II, pp. 25-28.
28. Huxley, L., *Life and Letters of T. H. Huxley*, 1900, p. 18.
29. *University of London Calendars*, 1854-64.
30. *University of Cambridge Local Examinations Report and Tables*, 1878.
31. *University of London Calendars*, 1869-1899.
32. Huxley, L. *Life and Letters of Sir Joseph Dalton Hooker*, Vol. I, 1918.
33. *Ibid.*
34. Gilmour, John, *British Botanists*, 1944, p. 44.
35. Hooker, J. D., *Botany*, 1876. This was one of a series of science primers written for use of Government Science Classes at South Kensington and associated institutions.
36. *Science and Art Department Pass Lists*, 1863 includes under Botany: Apothecary (20 yrs.), Assistant Draper (18 yrs.), son of Tailor (13 yrs.), Methodist Minister (51 yrs.), Assistant Teacher (17 yrs.), Clerk (16 yrs.), Medical Student (18 yrs.), Tea Urn Maker (27 yrs.), Gardener (26 yrs.), Son of Pawnbroker (12 yrs.).
37. *Report of Science and Art Department*, 1874.
38. Mumford, A. A., *The Manchester Grammar School*, 1515-1915, p. 339.
39. *College of Preceptors' Pupils' Examinations*, 1880-1900.

CHAPTER SIX   Adult Education in the Village—Exhibitions and Expeditions

1. General agricultural background information for the period has been derived largely from Ernle, Lord R.E.P. *English Farming Past and Present*, 1936.
2. Board of Agriculture, *Agricultural Survey of Suffolk*, 1797.
3. Obituary of "The Reverend Professor Henslow" in *Gardeners' Chronicle*, 8th June 1861.
4. Obituary of J. S. Henslow, in *Proceedings of Linnaean Society*, Vol. 2, 1861.
5. A copy of this *Address* is held by Cambridge University Library.
6. *Bury and Norwich Post*, 13th November, 1844.
7. *Ibid.*, 20th November, 1844.
8. Henslow, George, *Reminiscences of a Scientific Suffolk Clergyman*, No. 6, "Allotments and Horticultural Shows" in *Eastern Counties Magazine and Suffolk Notebook*, November 1901.
9. Jenyns, L., *Memoirs of the Reverend John Stevens Henslow*, 1862, p. 74.
10. Barlow, N. (ed.) *Darwin and Henslow*, 1967, p. 165.
11. Jenyns, *op. cit.*, pp. 95-9.
12. Hitcham Horticultural Shows were reported in *Gardeners' Chronicle* for 1854, 1856, 1857, 1859. The editor Henslow's friend and London colleague Professor John Lindley, greatly admired Henslow's work with the Hitcham villagers and was pleased to give it generous coverage in his journal.
13. Copy of the handbill is with *Henslow Papers* from Hitcham Parish Church.

14. This was the year of the Great Exhibition held at Crystal Palace. The inclusion of this exhibit illustrates Henslow's determination to educate villagers in contemporary affairs outside their parish boundaries.

15. In the October handbill, Henslow states:
"A ladder at the East end will accommodate those who are too lazy to go round by the gate; but no one is to act unneighbourly by walking through hedges."

16. *Henslow Papers.* Henslow sent a number of handbills and reports on village ventures to one Thomas Martin, a surgeon living at Reigate, who founded and worked hard to support the Mechanics' Institute there.

17. Reeve, Lovell, "A Village Flower Show". This extract is from the reprint in *Proceedings of the Linnaean Society,* Volume 6, 1853.

18. *Henslow's Correspondence,* Kew.

19. *Ibid.*

20. "Village Horticultural Show" in *Gardeners' Chronicle,* 24th September, 1859. Professor Lindley, in conjunction with George Bentham, had organised the first flower shows of the Horticultural Society (later the Royal Horticultural Society) from 1830. With this successful experience behind him, Lindley's praise of the Hitcham shows could not be ignored.

21. "Bree Letters" in *Henslow's Letters,* 1850-1858, Ipswich Museum.

22. Parish Accounts 1855 in *Hitcham Papers,* Ipswich Public Library.

23. *Henslow's Letters,* Ipswich.

24. *Ibid.*

25. *Ib.*

26. *Gardeners' Chronicle,* 24th September, 1859.

27. Jenyns, *op. cit.,* pp. 97-9.

28. Parish Accounts, 1841 in *Hitcham Papers,* Ipswich Public Library.

29. *Bury and Norwich Post,* 31st July 1841.

30. "Address to Inhabitants of Hitcham" Easter Week, 1849 in *Henslow Papers,* Bury.

31. *Henslow Papers.*

32. Parish Accounts, 1859 in *Hitcham Papers.*

33. *Henslow Papers.*

34. List of books in Hitcham Library, *Henslow Papers.*

35. Roget's *Bridgewater Treatise* explores the arguments of philosophers in the science and religion controversy. The volumes would explain Henslow's standpoint to any of his flock able and willing to read them.

36. A questionnaire in manuscript form is included in *Hitcham Papers,* Ipswich. The quotation in the text is taken from the section on lending libraries.

37. Henslow, Geo., *Reminiscences of a Scientific Suffolk Clergyman,* No. VII. "Village Excursions" in *Eastern Counties Magazine and Suffolk Notebook,* February 1902.

38. Jenyns, *op. cit.,* p. 115, Jenyns quotes Henslow's own account of 1849 excursion.

39. Henslow, Geo., *Reminiscences:* VII.

40. *Henslow Papers.* The postscript was added in Henslow's own hand.

41. The report is taken from the cutting of a newspaper printed by Stephen Piper, Old Buttermarket, Ipswich, Tuesday July 31st 1849. The cutting is with the *Henslow Papers* at Bury St Edmund's Record Office.

42. *Henslow Papers.*

43. Jenyns, *op. cit.,* pp. 118-120.

44. Dr Clarke's letter of resignation is attached to minutes of 3.1.1851 in *Minute Book,* Ipswich Museum.

45. Henslow, Geo. *Reminiscences:* VII.

46. Henslow, J. S. "Excursion" in *Gardeners' Chronicle,* 1850, p. 629.

47. Henslow, Geo., *Reminiscences:* VII.

48. *Henslow's Letters,* Ipswich.

49. Henslow, J. S. "Excursion" in *Gardeners' Chronicle,* 1850, p. 629.

50. *Henslow Papers.*

51. Henslow, Geo., *Reminiscences:* VII.

52. Jenyns, *op. cit.*, p. 120.
53. Henslow, Geo., *Reminiscences:* VII.
54. The "Programme" ran to eleven printed pages. A copy is available in Cambridge University Library. In addition Henslow circulated to participants some maps of Cambridge, plates of the Colleges and pictures of 200 of the most interesting plants in the Botanic Gardens.
55. Babington, C. C. *Memorials, Journal & Botanical Correspondence,* 1897, p. 174.
56. *Henslow's Letters,* Ipswich.
57. Henslow, Geo., *Reminiscences:* VII.
58. Already in August 1855 charges were rising. Henslow confided to Knights on 2nd August 1855.
    "I have only just heard from Dr. D. that our boat is the River Queen the same as we have had three times before—He says they now charge 2d per head for landing at Landguard Fort—but we have never had any difficulty about getting ashore by a plank—I can't now ask people for any more and I have fewer applicants than usual for the tickets on account of the lateness of the hay harvest . . ."

CHAPTER SEVEN   Science and the Farmers

1. Jenyns, L., *Memoir of the Reverend John Stevens Henslow,* 1862, p. 70.
2. It is interesting to note that Henslow had risked annoying the farmers even on this occasion by concluding his address with a reminder to his captive audience,
    "You have the proper cultivation of your labourers to look too. This is not the place, nor is this the befitting occasion (not speaking as a priest here) for one to appeal to you on any higher grounds than mere worldly policy, for the commanding attention to their moral, intellectual and social condition. One of the best manures which you can provide for the description of culture I now allude to, is to serve your labourers constant employment."
    Quoted in Jenyns, *op. cit.*, p. 85.
3. *Letters to the Farmers of Suffolk with a Glossary of Terms used.* London, 1843. A copy is in Cambridge University Library. The address to the Hadleigh Club is a prefix to the volume.
4. Henslow, J. S., "To the Farmers of Suffolk"—Letter I in *Bury and Norwich Post,* 11th January 1843.
5. Bree, Letter in *Bury and Norwich Post,* 1st February 1843 Bree's comments are given at close of Henslow's "Letter IV".
6. The Professor of Agriculture and Chemistry at Oxford University, Dr Daubney, later apologised for misleading Henslow and the apology was included in Henslow's "Letter IX", *Bury and Norwich Post,* 8th March 1845.
7. Henslow "Letter XI", *Bury and Norwich Post,* 22nd March 1843.
8. *Ibid.*
9. Henslow encouraged country gentry and rural clergy to improve agriculture by trying experiments arising from the works of Sir John Hepschell, de Canddle, Liebig, Lindley, Johnson and Sir Humphrey Dave—see "Letter XV", *Bury and Norwich Post,* 26th April 1843.
10. The *Bury and Norwich Post,* 15th March 1843, contains the detailed reports of three experiments undertaken by Messrs Hitchcock, Pilgrim (of Hitcham) and Carter.
11. Henslow "Letter XIV", *Bury and Norwich Post,* 19th April 1843.
12. Jenyns, *op. cit.*, pp. 193-204. The pages gave a detailed account of Henslow's work in the field.
13. Henslow, George, *Reminiscences of a Scientific Suffolk Clergyman.* I, "Natural History" in *Eastern Counties Magazine and Suffolk Notebook.* August 1900.
14. *Henslow Papers* from Hitcham Parish Church.
15. *Ibid.*
16. "Bree Letters" in *Henslow's Letters, 1850-1858,* Ipswich Museum.

CHAPTER EIGHT   Museums for the People

1. Jenyns, L., *Memoir of the Reverend John Stevens Henslow,* 1862, p. 150.
2. *Ibid.,* p. 8.
3. Clark and Hughes (ed.), *Life and Letters of Adam Sedgwick,* 1890, p. 222.
4. The audits quoted here are taken from Clark and Hughes, *op. cit.,* p. 234.
5. *Ibid.,* p. 207.
6. Jenyns, *op. cit.* Ch. 2.
7. Huxley, L. *Life and Letters of Joseph Dalton Hooker,* 1918.
8. *Henslow Correspondence,* Kew Herbarium and Library.
9. One of the less successful "longer" though interesting expositions features on a bill sent to Martin for an autumn show two years previously. It featured: 3 p.m. Mr. Henslow to explain the views of Sir B. Brodie, in the manner in which some vegetable poisons (Wavari, Upas-ticute, Alcohol, Prussic Acid, Oil of Tobacco, etc.) act upon the Brain; whilst others (Upas-artiar, Infusion of Tobacco etc.) act upon the Heart. He will further give an account of the following remarkable poisons
   (1) Wavari, of the Indians of Guiana—Arrows and Blowpipe. Nux-vomica—Strychnine.
   (2) Tanguin-nut, of Madagascar—Superstitions and cruelties of natives.
   (3) Upas-artiar, and Upas-ticute of Java—False stories and true, history of these. Bread fruit and Cow-tree.
   (4) Prussic acid—Opium etc.
   see Handbill in *Henslow Papers,* Hitcham.
10. Barlow, Nora (ed.) *Darwin and Henslow,* 1967, Letter 61.
11. *Henslow Correspondence,* Kew.
12. Henslow was currently engaged in a campaign to establish a Natural Science Tripos at Cambridge and Jenyns claims in the *Memoir* that Henslow, while preparing this *Address,* had received news that the opposition was beginning to relent. He was apparently keen to press home the advantage.
13. Jenyns, *op. cit.,* pp. 156-7.
14. Henslow's description of George Ransome, pharmacist, to Thomas Martin on 10th November 1849 in a letter in *Henslow Papers,* Hitcham. Ransome's zeal was, alas, to prove his downfall in the Museum's affairs.
15. The British Association's President, George Biddell Airy, Astronomer Royal, referred to this engineering achievement in his opening address at the Ipswich Meeting with the following complimentary remarks:
   "It is known to many members of the Association that this instrument was constructed in this town by Messrs. Ransome and May; and for the admirable proportions of its various parts, for the firmness of fitting and of the few portions of which it is composed and for the accuracy of the external forms of work etc. it may well be considered as one of the first specimens of engineering that has ever been produced."
   from *Report of British Association for the Advancement of Science,* 1851.
16. Papers with local relevance included Sir Charles Lyell, F.R.S. "On the Occurrence of a Stratum of Stones covered with Barnacles in the Red Crag at Whenstead near Ipswich." Professor Owen, F.R.S. "On Fossil Mamonatia of the Red Crag".
   Mr Charles May (local Secretary of the British Association and member of the Ipswich engineering firm involved in the Greenwich Observatory telescope), "On Application of Chilled Cast Iron to the Pivots of Astronomical Instruments". Specimens were demonstrated.
17. *Ipswich Museum Minutes,* 30th August 1852.
18. *Ibid.,* Annual Report, December 1852.
19. *Ib.,* 1st November, 1852.
20. *Ib.*
21. Henslow, J. S. Letter of acceptance attached to *Minutes,* 16th June 1855.
22. Subscriptions included Professor Faraday £5; Dr Whewell £1; C. Darwin £1 1s 0d; J. S. Bowerbank £5; Professor Henslow £5; E. S. Austin £20; Lovell Reeve £10.
23. Manuscript is attached to *Ipswich Museum Minutes,* 3.1.1851.

24. Henslow's reply is also attached to *Ipswich Museum Minutes*, 3.1.1851.
25. *Ipswich Museum Minutes*, 5th Anniversary Meeting, 15th December 1852.
26. "Bree Letters" in *Henslow's Letters*, Ipswich Museum.
27. *Henslow Correspondence*, Kew.
28. *Henslow's Letters*, Ipswich.
29. *Ibid.*
30. *Ipswich Museum Minutes*, 13.10.1853.
31. *Henslow Letters*, 1850-1858. Ipswich Museum.
32. Correspondence between Henslow and George Knights is to be found in *Henslow's Letters*, 1850-1858, Ipswich Museum. They are quoted extensively in this chapter.
33. The importance of the Crag Fossils had been brought to attention of local scientists at the British Association Meeting, Ipswich, 1851.
34. Henslow's uncertainty of date was now due to a lack of reply from Rigaud with whom he hoped to stay. This man was a master at Ipswich Grammar School and for some time very active on the museum's management committee. Letter writing was however, not a strong point for several times Henslow's plans were held up for want of Rigaud's replies.
35. Professor Richard Owen was at this time Hunterian Professor of Comparative Anatomy at the Royal College of Surgeons.
36. Gray, J. E. was keeper of the zoological section of the British Museum. The "Letter" quoted here is in the *Henslow Correspondence*, Kew.
37. Jenyns, *op. cit.*, pp. 159-160.
38. "Bree Letters".
39. L. Huxley, *Life and Letters of Joseph Dalton Hooker*, 1918, p. 434.
40. Lyon Playfair's letters to Henslow on this subject are in the *Henslow Correspondence*, Kew.
41. *Reports of the British Association for the Advancement of Science*, 1854.
42. *Ibid.*, pp. 108-9.
43. *Ib.* The Report of Henslow's Committee is printed pp. 110-126. Henslow's committee was allocated a further £10 in each of the years 1856 and 1857 to collect lists of Typical Objects for the sections missing in the 1855 Report.
44. Jenyns had been taken by Henslow to see other Museums including Bristol and was well aware of the Professor's aims for a provincial museum.
45. *Henslow Papers*, Hitcham.
46. "Bree Letters".
47. Lardner's *Cabinet Cyclopaedia* contained articles showing the application of science to everyday life and was written in popular style and published in 133 volumes.
48. In February 1858 his lecture was "On the Application of Science in the Manufacture of Candles from Animal, Vegetable and Mineral Products". A local firm, Price's had sent him stages in candle making to illustrate the lecture. One of the 1859 lectures, 20th January, was "On the Organic Compounds prepared for Plants from the deterioration of Animals".
49. *Ipswich Museum Minutes*, 17th January 1854. See Chairman's Report.

CHAPTER NINE   A Reflection

1. Henslow, J. S., *Illustrations to be employed in Practical Lessons on Botany; adapted to beginners of all classes*, 1858.
2. The letter of which this is an extract was written to Hooker's friend Dr Thomas Anderson in Calcutta and is reproduced in L. Huxley's *Life and Letters of Sir Joseph Dalton Hooker*, Volume 2, 1918, p. 61.

Index

A

Accessions, 107
adult literacy classes, 11, 83
agriculture, 74, 90
 (*see also* Royal Agricultural Society)
allotment scheme, 12, 30, 33, 34, 75, 76, 79, 80, 91
apparatus (*see* botany teaching)
archaeological finds, 110
arithmetic, 37, 38, 52, 53
Arnold, Matthew, 27
Athenaeum, 117
attendance (school), 35, 40, 42, 45

B

Babington, Charles Cardale, 9, 17, 18, 20, 26, 89, 114
Baker, Marianne, 38
 —Susan, 38, 46
baptist dissenters, 90
Barnard, Major, 47
 —Mrs, 11, 60
Beagle, 10, 13, 21, 23, 100
benefit clubs (*see* clubs)
Bentham, George, 50
Berkeley, Miles J, 9, 19, 95, 114
Bildeston 35, 120
botany, 9, 16, 22, 27, 38, 42, 43, 50, 51, 62, 71, 98
 —economic, 14, 44, 56, 65
 —geographical, 44, 56
 —historical, 44, 56
 —physiology, 56, 65, 72
 —structural, 56, 65
 —systematic, 44, 57, 65
botany gardens
 —Cambridge, 24, 25, 26, 89, 98, 120
 —school, 60, 68
Botany, Regius Chair of, 10, 15, 98
botany teaching
 41, 42-59, 60-69
 (*see also* volunteer class)
 —apparatus, 43
 —bottlerack, 45, 66
 —deal board, 68
 —dissecting needles, 43, 58, 68
 —handlens, 43, 68, 76
 —penknife, 43, 70
botanical nosegay, 47, 77
Bottisham Hall, 10, 15
Bowerbank, J. Scott, 102, 114
Bree, Charles, 80, 106, 107, 108, 116

Bridgewater Treatises, 13, 51, 83
British Association for the Advancement of Science, 13, 66, 67, 68, 76, 102, 114, 115, 119
 —Report on Typical Forme for Museums, 114
British Museum, 10, 97
Bunbury, Sir H., 75

C

Camberwell, Dr Jephson's, 10
Cambridge Philosophical Society, 15, 21, 22, 23, 98
Cambridge Syndicate, 27
cataloguing, 10, 97, 101
Chair, of mineralogy, 10
 —of botany, 10
chemistry, 15
children's pence, 31, 35, 40
Cholsey-cum-Moulsford, 11
Christian belief, 11, 13, 43
Christian charity, 32
Clarendon Commission, 18, 62, 66, 67
classics, 25
 —classical teaching, 57
classification, 13, 22, 60
 —Linnean, 65
clubs (benefit), 29, 30, 31, 96
collecting, 10, 15, 97, 101
collections, 99, 101, 109, 111
College of Preceptors, 69
Committee of Council on Education, 37, 53, 54
coprolites, 95
Corn Laws, 12, 74, 94
Corpus Christi College, 12
crag fossils, 108
Crystal Palace, 78
Cummings, Professor James, 15
curate, 11
curator, 37, 104, 107

D

Darwin, Charles, 9, 10, 13, 18, 19, 20, 21, 22, 23, 27, 31, 47, 48, 49, 57, 76, 100
Darwin Erasmus, 27
Dawes, Dean, 19, 36, 42
deductive thinking, 22
demonstrations, 15, 16, 106
Department of Science and Art, 42, 44, 52, 60, 69, 112

Devonshire Commission, 18, 74, 69
diagrams, 60, 62, 64, 67, 68
disorderly behaviour, 104, 105
distress, 116
Downing Hall, 90
drawings, 16, 44, 52, 61, 119

E
East India Company, 70, 71, 107
Easter Term, 24
elementary schools, 60, 62, 63, 73
English, 57
Ennals, Robert, 32, 39, 40
entomology, 18
evolutionary theory, 22
examinations, 11, 36, 37, 52, 54, 68-73
examination boards,
 —Cambridge University, 69
 —junior, 70
 —senior, 70
 —College of Preceptors, 69, 72
 —East India Company (medical service),
 70, 71
 —London University, 69
 —General Examination for Women,
 70
 —Intermediate B.Sc., 70
 —Matriculation, 69
 —Preliminary Scientific, 70
 Science and Art Department, 71, 72
excursions,
 —field, 18, 45, 46, 65
 —geological, 15
 —village, 11, 84, 87, 88, 89, 90
experiments, 24, 91, 93, 94
experimental work, 60, 72
Eye, 38

F
Faculty psychology, 56
farmers, 30, 46, 74, 76, 88, 89, 90, 91-96,
 119
Felixstowe, 95
Feoffment Charities, 34, 35, 39
fertilisers, 12
field excursions, 18, 45, 46, 65
fireworks, 75
Fitch, Walter, 61
flora, of Suffolk, 46
 —(overseas), 13, 21, 22, 25
floral specimens, 16, 63, 72, 73
forays, 10, 15, 19
Forbes, Professor E., 101, 114
fossils, 19, 96, 108, 110

"freenights", 104, 105, 106
freetraders, 88
French, 20
fresh material, 17

G
Gamlingay, 18
geography, 37, 52
geology, 15
Gosling, Maria, 38, 46
government scholars, 38
grammar, 37, 52
grants, 35, 36, 39, 40, 53
Great Exhibition 1851, 42, 89, 107
Gregory, Rev. Tighe, 31
guano, 77, 79
gypsum, 92, 94

H
Hadleigh, 35
Hadleigh Farmers' Club, 12, 91, 94, 95
"hard words", 58, 60, 68
Harvey, Lord A., 117
Harwich, 85, 86
Henslow, Sir John, 10
 —Frances, 11, 50, 83
 —George, 11, 67, 72
Her Majesty's Inspectors (of schools),
 (see Inspectors of Schools)
herbarium, 17, 44, 45, 62, 65, 108, 109
 —Kew, 99
 —Lemann, 99
higher grade schools, 72
history, 52
Hitcham Labourers' and Mechanics'
Home and Colonial College, 37
Horticultural Society, 77, 79
Hooker, Joseph Dalton, 11, 22, 23, 63, 66,
 67, 72, 99, 113, 114, 120
 —Sir William, 25, 99, 100
horticultural shows, 12, 47, 76, 78, 81, 119
H.R.H. Prince Albert, 42, 63, 64, 102, 103
Huxley, Thomas Henry, 13, 69, 72, 114
Hyde Park, 73
hypothesis, 22, 23, 24
 (see also laws, working)

I
Illustrations, 18, 64
illustrative material, 64, 65
inductive (thinking), 22
insects, 10

Inspectors of Schools, 35, 37, 38, 39, 52, 53, 54, 63
investigation, Scientific, 17, 22, 43, 49, 65, 69
investigatory methods, 72
Ipswich Museum, 11, 27, 101-118
—committee, 102
—debt, 104
—library, 106
—management committee, 104
—president, 101, 102, 103, 104
—subscribers, 97, 102, 103, 104
Isle of Anglesea, 15, 98
Isle of Man, 21, 98

J
Jenyns, Rev. George, 10
Jenyns, Harriet, 10
Jenyns, Leonard, 15, 19, 115

K
Kew gardens, 73, 89
Kirby, William, 13, 97, 101
Kitchener, F. E., 68
Knights, George, 37, 43, 45, 81, 107, 108

L
Labelling, 111
Land Improvement Society, 76
Landguard Fort, 88
Lankester, Professor Edwin, 102, 114
Lardiners' Cyclopaedia, 115
laws, working, 22, 24, 51
Leach, Dr, 10
Lectures, 11, 15, 16, 17, 18, 24, 27, 54, 63, 64, 67, 81, 91, 96, 101, 115
—museum, 115, 116, 117
—preparation, 17, 54, 115
lecturets, 100
liberal awakening, 12
liberal education, 22, 25, 38, 57
library, Parish, 30, 83
Liebig, Justice, 65, 92
Lindlay, Professor John, 25, 47, 62, 69, 80
Lowe, Robert, 62
Lyell, Charles, 21, 27, 51

M
Mackintosh, Sir J., 19
magisterial duties, 12
marble bust (J. S. Henslow), 99, 119
marriage, 10

Martin, Thomas, 78
mathematics, 15, 25
medal, 113
medical men, 69, 71
—students, 70
Melbourne, Lord, 12
methods—of science, 21, 24
mineralogy, 15
—Chair of, 10, 15, 98
minerals, 110
Mitchell, Rev. M., 35
models, 17, 68, 112, 113
molluscs, 10
Monday lessons (*see* botany teaching)
monitor, 36
monitorial system, 36
Moral Science Tripos, 27
museums—botanical (Cambridge), 98
—marquee, 81, 99
—Ipswich, 11, 27, 85, 101-118
—Kew, 99
—South Kensington, 45, 62
—Woodwardian, 15, 97, 98
—zoological (Cambridge), 98
museums, typical forms for, 114

N
National Society for promoting the Education of the Poor in the Principles of the Established Church, 32, 35, 36, 39
natural history, 11, 16, 19, 20, 51, 67, 77, 97, 98, 106
natural history museum, ideal, 101
natural history sciences, 15, 25, 27, 63
natural sciences, 26
Natural Science Tripos, 10, 25, 27, 28, 29
naturalist, 1

O
observations, 17, 21, 22, 23, 43, 63, 64
Oliver, Professor David, 44, 68, 69
Organised Science Classes, 72
Origin of Species, 13, 22, 24
Orphan Asylum, Clapton, 54
Owen, Richard, 22, 64, 110

P
Palmerston, Lord, 12
pamphlet—*Illustrations to be employed in Practical Lesson on Botany adapted to Beginners* by J. S. Henslow, 66, 119
Paris Exhibition, 1855, 112, 113
payment by results, 62

phosphate nodules, 95
photosynthesis, 65, 72, 94
physiology, 43
Playfair, Lyon, 61, 62, 74, 112, 113
political bribery, 12
polytechnic (London), 89
popular education, 31, 33, 34, 36
popular instruction, 106
popular science education, 15, 117
post, 45
postal services, 13
potato crop, 95
practical examinations, 62, 73
practical exercises, 16, 18
Prime Minister, 27
private schools, 60, 72
prizes, 12, 43, 44, 47, 76, 77, 78, 79, 80
proprietary schools, 60, 72
protectionists, 88
Public Libraries and Museums Act, 1850, 104
public schools, 22, 60, 66
pupil-teachers, 37, 38, 40, 41, 53, 54, 119

Q
Queen's Scholarship, 53

R
rail, 25
rail travel, 13
railways, 84, 90
Ransome Family, 84
Ransome, George, 32, 102, 103
Ransome Ironworks, 84
Ransome, Messrs, 40
Ransome, Mr, 76
Ransome and May, Messrs, 102
Ray Club, 20
rector, 11, 28, 29-41
red clover, 95
red cragg, 95
Reeve, Lovell, 78
Regius Chair of Botany, 10, 16, 25
religion, 26, 101
—science v., 13, 24, 51, 56
religious teaching, 52
research, 22
Revised Code, 1867, 62
Richardson, Miss, 36, 44
Richmond Park, 73
Rochester, mathematical school, 10
Roman tesselated pavement, 116
romantic movement, 14

Romilly, John, 27
Rothamstead Experimental Station, 74
Royal Agricultural Society, 12, 74
royal children, 9, 42, 63
Royal Commissions
—Clarendon 1862, 66, 67
—Devonshire 1874, 69
royal lessons, 63, 65
Royal School of Mines, 72

S
St John's College, Cambridge, 10, 14, 15
St Mary the Less, Cambridge, 10
schedules
—(agriculture), 93
—(botany), 43, 45, 50, 58, 59, 60, 64, 67
Schools
Bath High, 70
Bedford College, 70
Bildeston, 35, 120
Camberwell, Dr Jephson's, 10
Charterhouse, 9
Cheltenham, 69
Cheltenham Grammar, 70
Cheltenham Ladies, 70
Church of St Saviour's, 72
Clifton, 68, 69
Epsom College, 70
Hitcham
—Dame, 31
—Parish, 9, 11, 30, 31-41, 91
Manchester Grammar, 7
Manchester High, 70
Marlborough College, 67, 68, 69
Mercers', 70
Mount, York, 70
Needham Grammar, 69
Newcastle-under-Lyme Grammar, 68, 70
North London Collegiate, 72
Nottingham Girls' High, 70
Nottingham High, 70
Queen's College, 70
Rochester Mathematical, 10
Rugby, 67, 69
Sheffield Royal Grammar, 70
St Paul's, 69, 70
Taunton, 68, 69
Winchester, 69
Schoolmistress, 33, 34, 36, 37, 38, 40, 54
science, v. religion, 13, 24, 51, 56
Science Museum, 62
scientific education, 10, 42, 57
scientific method, 11, 15, 24, 91, 92, 94

scientific thinking, 22, 42, 43, 57
scientific terms, 68
Sedgewick, Professor Adam, 10, 11, 15, 19, 20, 21, 22, 97
self-help, 23, 29, 30, 32
senate (Cambridge), 24, 25, 27, 29
sermon, 12, 33, 34, 41, 83, 91
Sewell, Harriet, 37, 46, 47, 53
Society for the Propagation of Useful Knowledge, 14, 17, 44
soirees, 10, 19, 21
South Kensington Museum, 45, 62
Sparrow Charity, 34, 35, 39, 40
specimens, floral, 11, 17, 55, 64, 65, 112
spelling, 53, 57
Stoke and Melford Benefit Society, 85
Stowmarket, 84

T
teaching, 11, 16, 17, 19, 54, 63, 64, 119
technical terms, 50
Thackeray, William Makepeace, 27
tithe dinners, 88, 89
training colleges, 62
transpiration, 65, 72
Tuckwell, Rev. W., 68
tutor, 20, 21

U
unemployment, 34, 74
useful knowledge, 13, 17, 44

—society for the propagation of, 14, 17, 44
Uredo (wheat fungus), 95

V
vandalism, 105
village craftsmen, 111
—blacksmith, 111, 112
—carpenter, 112
village machinery, 62, 65, 111
volunteer class, 9, 37, 41-59
(see also botany teaching)

W
Walker's Lecturer, 25
Wheat fungus, 95
Whewell, William, 10, 13, 19, 21, 22, 25
Whitelands College, 37
Wilson, James, 67
Woodwardian Museum, 15, 97, 98
writing, 37, 57

Y
Young Men's Association, Ipswich, 85

Z
Zoology, 15
Zoological gardens (London), 89
Zoological Museum (Cambridge), 98

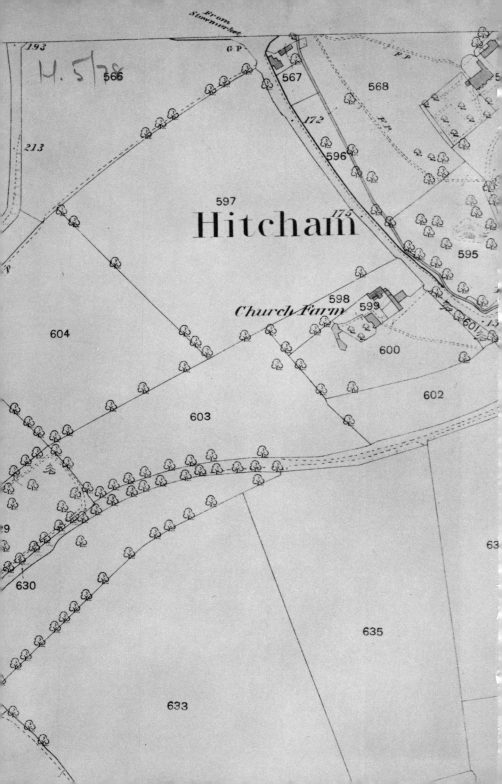